FOURIER TRANSFORMS
AND X-RAY DIFFRACTION

FOURIER TRANSFORMS
AND X-RAY DIFFRACTION

By

H. LIPSON
D.Sc., M.A., F.Inst.P., F.R.S.
PROFESSOR OF PHYSICS

and

C. A. TAYLOR
B.Sc., Ph.D., F.Inst.P.
LECTURER IN PHYSICS

FACULTY OF TECHNOLOGY
UNIVERSITY OF MANCHESTER

LONDON
G. BELL AND SONS LTD
1958

QD 945
.L5

First published 1958

548
£767

PRINTED IN GREAT BRITAIN BY ROBERT MACLEHOSE AND CO. LTD
THE UNIVERSITY PRESS, GLASGOW

PREFACE

This monograph has been written with a definite objective in view – to produce an introduction to Fourier-transform theory that would serve as a basis for students who wish to apply the theory to X-ray diffraction. This objective is not new; Wrinch's well-known book – *Fourier Transforms and Structure Factors* – was published in 1946. But Wrinch's book, we think, is rather too formal to appeal to non-mathematicians; we have therefore tried to relate the mathematics more closely to physical principles, sometimes sacrificing complete mathematical rigidity. Understanding of this book does not therefore depend upon a grasp of, for example, the Fourier-transform theory contained in such books as that of Titchmarsh.

Our interest in Fourier transforms first arose because of the importance of the concept in understanding the application of optical-diffraction procedures to the determination of crystal structures. These procedures are not, however, given more than brief mention in this monograph, and we propose to deal with them in more detail in a further publication.

We firmly believe that the Fourier-transform approach simplifies the understanding of the diffraction of X-rays by crystals. We hope that this monograph will convince others of the validity of this claim.

H.L.
C.A.T.

v

ACKNOWLEDGEMENTS

In writing a monograph of this kind, ideas are drawn from a variety of sources, some of which are difficult to specify. Wherever possible we have given references but we are conscious that due acknowledgment may not always have been made. In particular, Dr. David Sayre's M.S. Thesis proved a fruitful source of inspiration, although no specific reference has been made to it. We also wish to acknowledge the help of a more concrete kind given by a number of our friends and colleagues. Dr. G. M. Bell made some helpful criticisms of the mathematical sections; Mr. B. J. Thompson helped in checking manuscripts and proofs and prepared the photographs in Appendix II; Mr. K. A. Morley organized the calculations for the transforms in Appendix I on the Manchester University Digital Computer, and Mr. E. Chambers prepared prints for reproduction from our original maps; Miss M. W. Allen typed the manuscript.

Acknowledgment is due to the following for permission to reproduce the diagrams named:

Proceedings of the Royal Society (fig. 17); Acta Crystallographica (figs. 37 and 65); Proceedings of the Physical Society (fig. 41); Journal of the Institute of Metals (fig. 50).

Finally, we should like to acknowledge the co-operation of the publishers, in particular of Mr. H. Hadaway, and the skill with which the drawings were prepared from our rough sketches.

H.L.

C.A.T.

NOTE

For ease of reference, all figures and equations carry the number of the page on which they appear. If there are two or more figures or equations on a page, they are numbered serially.

There is no name index, but the references are collected together at the end of the book and the pages on which they occur are given.

CONTENTS

CHAPTER 1

GENERAL OUTLINE

1. *Scattering of radiation by matter.* When radiation falls upon matter it is scattered; conversely, when we observe scattered radiation, we infer the existence of matter. These statements are true for most types of radiation, but under certain circumstances we may go further and deduce some of the properties of the object from the nature of the scattered radiation. From the radio waves received by radar equipment, the presence of an object at a particular point can be inferred and a limited amount of further information – its approximate size and speed, for example – may be deduced. One small range of wavelengths in the electromagnetic spectrum – visible light – has a much more important property, however; with it, by means of the eye, alone or aided by optical instruments, we can form an accurate image of the scattering object and so obtain precise evidence of its shape, colour, and other properties. But there is an inherent limit to the fineness of detail that can be observed in this way which is set by the wavelength of the radiation. If we wish to see detail on an atomic scale – which is roughly one-thousandth of the wavelength of visible light – it is necessary to use radiation of very much shorter wavelength and this falls right outside the visible region; several types of radiation can be used but none can be focused to give images with atomic detail. Other methods of image formation must be considered, and this monograph is chiefly concerned with the methods appropriate to the use of X-rays.

All the information from which the eye builds up an image is contained in the pattern of scattered light: the eye adds nothing; it merely interprets the pattern. It should, therefore, – at least in principle – be possible to interpret the pattern of scattered X-rays from an object and build up an 'image' which includes detail on the atomic scale. This interpretation is the essential problem in X-ray crystallography.

To construct the complete image, the angular distribution of intensity, frequency and phase of the scattered radiation must be known. Intensity and frequency are comparatively easy to determine, but relative phases are not. The eye avoids this problem by using directly the waves scattered by the object, the relative phases being preserved (the whole basis of the design of optical instruments can be summarized as attempts to preserve the relative phases of a set of scattered waves). X-rays, however, have a wavelength that is

1

too small for direct use of the waves to be possible and thus any form of 'X-ray eye' or 'X-ray microscope' is impracticable. The difficulty of studying matter on the atomic scale by means of X-rays would therefore appear to be overwhelming, and for general irregular objects it is indeed so. Fortunately, however, on the atomic scale matter is not irregular; atoms tend to arrange themselves regularly and the regularity impresses itself on the pattern of scattered radiation.

For matter in the extreme condition of regularity – a crystal with a perfect lattice – the pattern of scattered radiation consists of a set of discrete beams, each produced in a particular direction with respect to both the incident beam of X-rays and the crystal. The rules governing the production of these scattered beams can be expressed in the form of Laue's equations or Bragg's equation, and since historically these equations initiated the subject they have naturally assumed a position of prominence in teaching. For many purposes they undoubtedly do form the best introduction; they correspond to the treatment of the ordinary diffraction grating in terms of the equation

$$n\lambda = d \sin \theta, \qquad (2.1)$$

and if one is interested solely in the wavelengths of spectral lines this treatment is satisfactory. But if one is interested in the fine structure of the grating elements, then the distribution of intensity in the different orders of diffraction becomes important and the scattering function of each element is involved. This function is the Fourier transform of the element.

For a crystal, emphasis lies almost entirely on the fine structure – the contents of the unit cell – and therefore the Fourier transform becomes of paramount importance. Instead, therefore, of starting with Laue's equations or Bragg's equation – both concerned with the crystal lattice – and introducing *later* the scattering function, we may consider first the scattering function and *then* its modification by the crystal lattice.

2. *The Fourier transform.* To determine the scattering function we suppose the unit-cell contents to be illuminated by a parallel beam of monochromatic X-radiation, and then find how the waves scattered from the various atoms add together. Each element of volume in the unit cell is assumed to scatter a wave with an amplitude proportional to the electron content, and the total wave scattered has an amplitude given by integrating the separate waves, taking into account the path differences associated with the separate elements. Each path difference depends upon the direction of the incident and diffracted waves and upon the position of the element

of volume with respect to a particular point chosen as origin.

It might therefore be supposed that there are three variables to be considered – the direction of the incident beam, the direction of the diffracted beam, and the position of the diffracting element. In fact, however, the first two can be reduced to a single vector of variable length bisecting the two directions; the required path difference is a function of this vector and that giving the position of the diffracting element with respect to the origin.

We shall show in the next chapter that, if $\rho(\mathbf{r})$ is the electron density in the volume element dV at a vector distance $\mathbf{r}$ from the origin, the total wave scattered relative to that scattered by a single electron placed at the origin is given by

$$G(S) = \int \rho(\mathbf{r}) \exp 2\pi i \mathbf{r} \cdot \mathbf{S} \, dV \qquad (3.1)$$

where S is the vector bisecting the incident and diffracted directions. $G(S)$ is the Fourier transform of the electron density and is, in general, a continuous function.

3. *Reciprocal space.* The vector S is defined in terms of the directions of the incident and diffracted waves. We may represent these two directions by vectors of arbitrary modulus, and it turns out to be simplest to make these moduli $\dfrac{1}{\lambda}$ where λ is the wavelength of

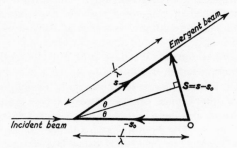

FIG. 3. Relationship between S, s, s_0 and θ. O is the origin of reciprocal space and $|\,s\,| = |\,s_0\,| = \lambda$.

the radiation. If s_0 and s are the two vectors concerned then S is defined as $s - s_0$ and from fig. 3 it can be seen that

$$|\,S\,| = \frac{2 \sin \theta}{\lambda} \qquad (3.2)$$

where 2θ is the angle of scattering.

The dimensions of $|\,S\,|$ are thus the reciprocal of a length and for this reason S is called a *reciprocal vector*. If s_0 is fixed, S varies in direction and length as s rotates. The end of the vector S passes through a region called *reciprocal space* – the space in which the Fourier transform is plotted.

The moduli of s_0 and s are chosen to be $\dfrac{1}{\lambda}$ in order to make S independent of λ. If the wavelength of the radiation is changed, for a given diffracted beam sin θ is proportional to λ, and thus $|S|$ is constant. The Fourier transform is thus characteristic of the electron-density distribution only and is not dependent upon the wavelength of the radiation. This fact is mentioned because for some purposes it is useful to retain λ (Bernal, 1926) by making $|s_0|$ unity; reciprocal space is then dimensionless, but the Fourier transform has a scale proportional to λ. In this monograph dimensionless reciprocal space will not be used.

4. *Combination of transforms.* It is not always necessary to consider the transform of the complete contents of a unit cell. Symmetry relationships, for example, may exist and a small portion of the unit cell may be the asymmetric unit, the rest being derived by successive application of the symmetry operations. These operations clearly have corresponding operations in reciprocal space and it becomes important to study the rules governing their correspondence. Similarly, groups of atoms may occur more than once without symmetry relationship, and rules governing the combination of their transforms will clearly be of great value. The corresponding operations are introduced in Chapter 3 and the most important pair – multiplication and convolution – is discussed fully in Chapter 4.

5. *The reciprocal lattice.* We have now introduced the idea of a scattering function which is continuous in reciprocal space. For a perfect crystal, this function is not observable throughout reciprocal space because interference occurs between waves scattered by the different unit cells and there is zero intensity except at specific points in reciprocal space. These points lie on a lattice called the *reciprocal lattice*, which is related to the crystal lattice in a way to be described in Chapter 3.

We may regard the X-ray diffraction pattern of a crystal as produced by the superposition of the Fourier transforms of the contents of the separate unit cells. These transforms cancel everywhere except at the reciprocal-lattice points; at these points they add together, and therefore the amplitude associated with any reciprocal-lattice point is proportional to the amplitude of the transform at that point. We may therefore regard the X-ray diffraction pattern of a crystal as the Fourier transform 'sampled' at the reciprocal-lattice points. This concept forms the basic idea in Fourier-transform theory as applied to X-ray diffraction.

This approach emphasizes one of the inherent difficulties of X-ray diffraction studies. We need information about the full Fourier transform of a unit cell but for a perfect crystal we can observe it experimentally only at certain points. On the other hand, it is impossible in practice to observe the scattering from a single unit cell or to interpret the scattering from a large number of identical but randomly arranged unit cells. The nearest approach is the work of Charlesby, Finch and Wilman (1939), who observed electron diffraction patterns of a large number of molecules arranged *parallel* to each other but with some randomness of position thermally produced. Intermediate conditions do, however, occur in practice. Crystals with limited imperfections give interpretable diffraction patterns and the Fourier-transform concept is an essential basis for study in this field. A section of the final chapter is devoted to this subject.

The transform approach also provides a direct introduction to the use of Fourier-synthesis techniques. It is natural to explore the mathematical counterpart of the production of an image by the eye from scattered beams of light, and the result – that the image is the Fourier transform of the Fourier transform – forms a basis for the introduction of the Fourier method of producing electron-density 'images' from X-ray diffraction data (Chapter 6).

CHAPTER 2

GROUP OR MOLECULAR TRANSFORM

1. *Phase relationships.* When a beam of radiation falls upon a body whose dimensions are small compared with the wavelength of the radiation, scattering (apart from the effects of polarization) takes place equally in all directions. The reason is that there are no appreciable path differences for waves scattered from different parts of the body, and thus, in every direction, the scattered waves are all in phase with each other. If, however, the dimensions of the body are not negligible, path differences arise; the scattered waves partially or wholly counteract each other, and thus different resultant intensities occur in different directions.

Let us suppose that we have a body with variable electron density $\rho(\mathbf{r})$ where $\mathbf{r}$ is the vector position of the point A_2 with respect to a

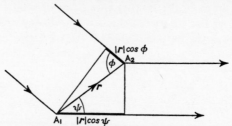

FIG. 6. Path difference for radiation incident at an angle with A_1A_2 and emergent at an angle ψ.

fixed point A_1 (fig. 6). Let the incident waves make an angle ϕ with $\mathbf{r}$ and let us consider the radiation scattered (not necessarily in the plane of the diagram) at an angle ψ with $\mathbf{r}$. Then the path difference for waves scattered by A_2 with respect to those scattered by A_1 is $|\mathbf{r}|(\cos\psi - \cos\phi)$. The phase difference is $\dfrac{2\pi|\mathbf{r}|}{\lambda}(\cos\psi - \cos\phi)$ since, if the path difference is λ, the phase difference is 2π.

2. *Scattering by a body of non-uniform density.* The element of volume around A_2 has an electron content $\rho(\mathbf{r})\,dV$; the expression for the scattered wave relative to the wave scattered by a single electron at the origin is thus

$$\rho(\mathbf{r})\,dV \exp\frac{2\pi i|\mathbf{r}|}{\lambda}(\cos\psi - \cos\phi) \qquad (6.1)$$

the complex exponential expression being used because it provides

6

the simplest mathematical way of denoting a wave of arbitrary phase. The total wave scattered by the body is then

$$\int \rho(\mathbf{r}) \exp \frac{2\pi i |\mathbf{r}|}{\lambda} (\cos\psi - \cos\phi) \, d\mathrm{V} \qquad (7.1)$$

the integral being taken over all the volume for which the electron density is finite.

The angles ϕ and ψ are measured spatially with respect to the vector $\mathbf{r}$. It is convenient, therefore, to use vector notation; $\frac{|\mathbf{r}| \cos\phi}{\lambda}$ is the scalar product of $\mathbf{r}$ and a vector $\mathbf{s}_0$ of modulus $\frac{1}{\lambda}$ in the direction of the incident beam, and $\frac{|\mathbf{r}| \cos\psi}{\lambda}$ is the scalar product of $\mathbf{r}$ and a vector $\mathbf{s}$ of modulus $\frac{1}{\lambda}$ in the direction of the diffracted beam. In the usual notation, the expression (7.1) is written

$$\int \rho(\mathbf{r}) \exp 2\pi i \mathbf{r} \cdot (\mathbf{s} - \mathbf{s}_0) \, d\mathrm{V}. \qquad (7.2)$$

This expression is the Fourier transform of the electron density and may be written as

$$G(\mathbf{S}) = \int \rho(\mathbf{r}) \exp 2\pi i \mathbf{r} \cdot \mathbf{S} \, d\mathrm{V} \qquad (7.3)$$

where $\mathbf{S} = \mathbf{s} - \mathbf{s}_0$.

The vector $\mathbf{S}$ has already been introduced (section 1.3) as a vector in reciprocal space; its properties will be discussed in more detail in Chapter 5. The function $G(\mathbf{S})$ therefore also exists in reciprocal space.

3. *Intensity of the scattered wave.* The intensity of a wave is proportional to the square of the amplitude. For a complex quantity it can be most simply evaluated by multiplying the quantity by its complex conjugate – the same function with the sign of the imaginary part reversed. If $G^*(\mathbf{S})$ is the complex conjugate of $G(\mathbf{S})$, then we may define a quantity called the ideal intensity I (Wilson, 1949*b*), which is given by the equation

$$I = G(\mathbf{S}) \cdot G^*(\mathbf{S}). \qquad (7.4)$$

I is related to the experimentally observed intensity by certain functions which depend on the conditions of observation and for which, in this monograph, we shall assume allowance has been made. (In single-crystal oscillation X-ray photographs, for example, the Lorentz and polarization factors are involved).

It is not possible to derive G(S) from measurements of I; only the modulus of G(S) can be derived. Thus it is impossible to derive the transform directly from experimental data.

4. *Atomic scattering factor.* Suppose that the scattering body is a single atom, undistorted by the presence of other atoms. We may then assume that the atom has spherical symmetry – that is, that $\rho(\mathbf{r})$ is a function of $|\mathbf{r}|$ only. G(S) therefore also has spherical symmetry and so is a function of $|S|$. Now $|S|$ is equal to $\dfrac{2 \sin \theta}{\lambda}$ (section 1.3); the radial distribution in the transform of an atom is thus identical with the *atomic scattering-factor curve* or f *curve* used in conventional treatment. We shall therefore use the symbol $f(S)$ for the transform of a single atom.

Since the electron density has been assumed to be spherically symmetric it is also centrosymmetric. Thus

$$f(S) = f^*(S) \qquad (8.1)$$

and therefore, from equation (7.4)

$$f(S) = I^{\frac{1}{2}}. \qquad (8.2)$$

In principle, we still cannot derive $f(S)$ unequivocally from this equation because we do not know whether to choose the positive or negative root. However we define $f(S)$ to be positive† when $|S| = 0$, and we know experimentally that it is a continuous function and that it does not pass through any zeros as $|S|$ increases; therefore it must remain positive throughout its observable range.

If an atom is not spherically symmetric its transform is no longer a function of $|S|$ only and can be truly represented only in three dimensions.

5. *Molecular scattering factor (or molecular transform).* Let us now consider a group of atoms. It is convenient to form a mental picture of this group as a chemical molecule and we shall often use such a picture in this monograph; but the theory applies to any group of atoms, whatever the chemical binding.

Let there be N atoms in the group, each with a scattering factor $f_n(S)$ and atomic co-ordinates x_n, y_n, z_n with respect to any convenient axes. Then the vector distance of the nth atom from the origin is

$$\mathbf{r}_n = \mathbf{x}_n + \mathbf{y}_n + \mathbf{z}_n, \qquad (8.3)$$

† Strictly, there is a change of phase when X-rays are scattered, but since this is the same for all atoms unless the wavelength of the radiation is near an absorption edge, we shall ignore the effect in this monograph. For neutrons, scattering factors may be negative.

and the expression for the wave scattered from the nth atom, relative to the origin of the unit cell, is

$$\int \rho(\mathbf{r}) \exp 2\pi i (\mathbf{r} + \mathbf{r}_n) \cdot \mathbf{S} \, dV$$

$$= \left\{ \int \rho(\mathbf{r}) \exp 2\pi i \mathbf{r} \cdot \mathbf{S} \, dV \right\} \exp 2\pi i \mathbf{r}_n \cdot \mathbf{S}$$

$$= f_n(\mathbf{S}) \exp 2\pi i \mathbf{r}_n \cdot \mathbf{S}. \tag{9.1}$$

The total scattered wave from the N atoms is thus, if we assume them to be of identical form,

$$G(\mathbf{S}) = \sum_{n=1}^{N} f_n(\mathbf{S}) \exp 2\pi i \mathbf{r}_n \cdot \mathbf{S}. \tag{9.2}$$

The summation sign is now used because we are considering a finite number of atoms, although each has a non-uniform electron density.

$G(\mathbf{S})$ is the Fourier transform of the group of atoms.

If, as explained in the previous section, the atoms can be regarded as spherically symmetric, the Fourier transform can be written as

$$G(\mathbf{S}) = \sum_{n=1}^{N} f_n \exp 2\pi i \mathbf{r}_n \cdot \mathbf{S} \tag{9.3}$$

and this is the form in which transforms are usually expressed. Practically, the equation corresponds to the assumption that the atoms are points, each having a scattering factor that decreases with angle.

Since the distribution of atoms is not spherically symmetric the transform can be represented only in three dimensions; nevertheless, it is essentially similar to the atomic scattering factor and has therefore been called the *molecular scattering factor* (Ewald, 1940; Knott, 1940) or *molecular transform* (Hettich, 1935).

6. *Representation of molecular transforms.* The representation of a transform in three dimensions is not straightforward, however, because in general it is complex; it is necessary to specify two quantities at each point – either the amplitude and phase or the real and imaginary parts. The latter is generally preferred in computational work and was used, for example, by Klug (1950*b*) in presenting the transform of the molecule triphenylene. The former is more usual in optical-transform work (See Appendices I and II).

When the molecule is centrosymmetric, the transform is real and thus only one diagram is necessary; in two dimensions, contours can be given (Appendix I) with some sort of distinction between

B

positive and negative values. Positive values indicate zero phase angle (scattered waves in phase with those scattered from a point at the origin) and negative values indicate a phase angle of π (scattered waves out of phase).

For a complete three-dimensional transform separate diagrams would have to be given of the contours at different levels. The authors do not know of any such computations. For plane molecules, however, if we assume purely point atoms (that is, no variation in scattering factor) the transform has identical sections parallel to the plane (Lipson and Cochran, 1953), and one section can be regarded as representing the three-dimensional transform. Since most transform work has been applied to plane molecules (Knott, 1940; Klug, 1950b; Lipson and Taylor, 1951; Stadler, 1953) this property has been much used.

7. *Influence of choice of origin.* It is important to appreciate that a description of a transform is dependent upon the choice of origin; for example, the transform of a centrosymmetric body is real only if the origin is taken at the centre of symmetry. Thus for a centrosymmetric grouping of atoms the centre of symmetry is always chosen as the origin. For a non-centrosymmetric molecule, however, there may be no obvious choice of origin and the real and imaginary

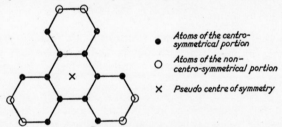

FIG. 10. Non-centrosymmetrical molecule with one large portion centrosymmetrical

parts are not absolute. Triphenylene (fig. 10) is not a good example of a non-centrosymmetric molecule; the molecule is partly centrosymmetric and the origin can be taken at the 'pseudo-centre'; the imaginary part of the transform is then generally weaker than the real part, being produced by only six atoms of the eighteen.

When there is no pseudo-symmetry of any sort, the choice of origin must be made on other grounds. It is wise to choose a point near to the centroid of the system; the further away, the more rapid will be the change of phase (Appendix I). Taking the origin halfway between two similar atoms may also be helpful, as then at least these two atoms have no contribution to the imaginary part of the transform.

Although the real and imaginary parts of a transform change according to the choice of origin, the modulus at any point is invariant. Since only the modulus is observable experimentally, there is no physical significance in the variation of the separate parts. (See Appendix I).

8. *Effect of molecular displacement.* We have seen in the previous section that the transform of a molecule is unique only in the distribution of modulus; the phase at any point is dependent upon the choice of origin. When two separate units scatter, their transforms superpose, but, as in all interference problems, the magnitude of the result at any point depends upon the relative phases at that point.

The variation of phase with origin can be seen by adding a constant vector $\mathbf{a}$ to all the vectors $\mathbf{r}_n$ specifying the atomic positions. The Fourier transform then becomes, from equation 9.3,

$$G_a(\mathbf{S}) = \sum_{n=1}^{N} f_n \exp 2\pi i \{(\mathbf{r}_n + \mathbf{a}) \cdot \mathbf{S}\}$$

$$= \sum_{n=1}^{N} f_n \exp 2\pi i \mathbf{r}_n \cdot \mathbf{S} \exp 2\pi i \mathbf{a} \cdot \mathbf{S}$$

$$= \exp 2\pi i \mathbf{a} \cdot \mathbf{S} \sum_{n=1}^{N} f_n \exp 2\pi i \mathbf{r}_n \cdot \mathbf{S}$$

$$= \exp 2\pi i \mathbf{a} \cdot \mathbf{S} \; G_0(\mathbf{S}) \qquad (11.1)$$

where $G_0(\mathbf{S})$ is the transform of the undisplaced molecule.

In words, we may say that the transform $G(\mathbf{S})$ is modified by a 'fringe function' $\exp 2\pi i \mathbf{a} \cdot \mathbf{S}$ which becomes finer as $\mathbf{a}$ increases. (The idea of fringes is essentially a two-dimensional one, but it is convenient to carry the term over also into three dimensions). The fringe function is not evident physically because the modulus of $\exp 2\pi i \mathbf{a} \cdot \mathbf{S}$ is always unity; it becomes evident only when two transforms are superposed. We can see, therefore, that phase is dependent upon position and, conversely, that the absolute position of a group of atoms can be found only if the relative phases of the different parts of its transform can be determined.

9. *Diffraction by more than one molecule.* Suppose there are two identical molecules in the same orientation separated by a vector distance $\mathbf{a}$. The composite transform is then

$$G_0(\mathbf{S}) + G_a(\mathbf{S})$$

$$= G_0(\mathbf{S}) (1 + \exp 2\pi i \mathbf{a} \cdot \mathbf{S}). \qquad (11.2)$$

The expression $1 + \exp 2\pi i \mathbf{a} \cdot \mathbf{S}$ is a fringe function modifying the amplitude. It has a modulus of 2 at every point for which $\mathbf{a \cdot S}$ is integral, and of zero for points half-way between, and so the total transform consists of the transform of one molecule crossed by a set of planar fringes.

The moduli of the transform at points for which $\mathbf{a \cdot S}$ is integral are equal to $2|G_0(\mathbf{S})|$. That is, the *relative* intensities at these points are the same as those for the transform of a single molecule.

If the two molecules are not in the same orientation the result is more complicated; the transforms of the two separate molecules are superimposed, but fringes, neither necessarily straight nor continuous, arise because of the phase relationships in the transforms. A number of special cases occur when the two molecules are related by crystallographic symmetry elements.

The most important example is provided by the centre of symmetry. The amplitude distributions (section 2.6) of two molecules so related are identical, but the phase distributions are not. The fringe system results from these differences in phase. As explained in section 2.7 we choose the centre of symmetry as origin; if the distance of this origin from an arbitrary point within the molecule (section 2.7) is $\mathbf{a}$, and if the Fourier transform with respect to this point is $G_0(\mathbf{S})$, then the transform with respect to the origin is (eq. *11*.1)

$$G_a(\mathbf{S}) = G_0(\mathbf{S}) \exp{(2\pi i \mathbf{a \cdot S})}. \qquad (12.1)$$

The transform of the second molecule with respect to the origin is

$$G_{-a}(\mathbf{S}) = G_0^*(\mathbf{S}) \exp{(-2\pi i \mathbf{a \cdot S})} \qquad (12.2)$$

since the corresponding arbitrary point is at distance $-\mathbf{a}$ from the origin and the coordinates with respect to the point are reversed. The total transform is thus

$$G_T(\mathbf{S}) = G_a(\mathbf{S}) + G_{-a}(\mathbf{S})$$

$$= G_0(\mathbf{S}) \exp{(2\pi i \mathbf{a \cdot S})}$$

$$+ G_0^*(\mathbf{S}) \exp{(-2i\pi \mathbf{a \cdot S})}. \qquad (12.3)$$

Now, $G_0(\mathbf{S})$ can be expressed as $|G_0| \exp{(i\phi_0)}$ where ϕ_0 is the phase angle (section 2.6) and thus $G_0^*(\mathbf{S}) = |G_0| \exp{(-i\phi_0)}$.

Therefore

$$G_T(\mathbf{S}) = |G_0| \{\exp{(i\phi_0)} \exp{(2\pi i \mathbf{a \cdot S})} + \exp{(-i\phi_0)} \exp{(-2\pi i \mathbf{a \cdot S})}\}$$

$$= |G_0| \{\exp{i(2\pi \mathbf{a \cdot S} + \phi_0)} + \exp{i(-2\pi \mathbf{a \cdot S} - \phi_0)}\}$$

$$= 2|G_0| \cos{(2\pi \mathbf{a \cdot S} + \phi_0)}. \qquad (12.4)$$

Thus, again, the modulus cannot exceed $2|G_0|$ and the relative values of the intensities at points for which $\cos{(2\pi \mathbf{a \cdot S} + \phi_0)} = 1$ are the same as the relative values at these points in the single transform. But the points satisfying this condition do not lie upon planes, or, in physical language, the fringes are no longer planar. Under certain conditions the fringes may have straight portions, corresponding to regions of approximately constant values of ϕ_0, but usually they are curved.

The same rules apply when more than two transforms of molecules related by different symmetry elements are added. It must always be remembered that, before addition, the transforms must be referred to a common origin.

10. *Summary of properties of transforms.* Before proceeding to diffraction by a complete crystal, it is useful to summarize the properties of Fourier transforms, as shown in the following table.

Operation in real Space	*Effect in Reciprocal Space*
Rotation about axis.	Rotation about parallel axis at same speed.
Change of scale in one direction.	Reciprocal change of scale in same direction.
Translation.	Modulus unchanged; phase modified by fringe function.
Addition of two or more units.	Vectorial summation of transforms referred to common origin.
E.g. two parallel units.	Transform for one unit crossed by parallel plane fringes; maximum amplitude doubled.
E.g. two centrosymmetrically related units.	Transform for one unit crossed by wavy fringes which may, in limited regions, be approximately plane.
Convolution of functions representing two distributions (see Chap. 4 and Appendix II).	Transform is product of separate transforms.

The relationships given in the table are completely reciprocal in that they still hold if the headings real space and reciprocal space are interchanged.

CHAPTER 3

DIFFRACTION BY A CRYSTAL

1. *Diffraction by a row of molecules.* In order to derive the diffraction pattern of the three-dimensional regular arrangement of molecules that constitutes a crystal, it is convenient first to consider a one-dimensional arrangement. Suppose that we have a row of M parallel molecules at equal distances $\mathbf{a}$ apart. If each molecule contains n atoms at positions $\mathbf{r}_n$, then the positions of all the atoms in the Mth molecule are specified by the vectors $m\mathbf{a} + \mathbf{r}_n$ where m is an integer ranging from 0 to M − 1.

The complete transform is then given by the equation

$$G_T(S) = \sum_0^{M-1} G_m(S)$$

$$= G_0(S)\,[1 + \exp 2\pi i \mathbf{a}\cdot\mathbf{S} + \ldots$$
$$\ldots + \exp 2\pi i m\mathbf{a}\cdot\mathbf{S}\ldots$$
$$\ldots + \exp 2\pi i(M-1)\,\mathbf{a}\cdot\mathbf{S}]. \qquad (14.1)$$

The series is geometric, the sum being

$$\frac{1 - \exp 2\pi i\,M\mathbf{a}\cdot\mathbf{S}}{1 - \exp 2\pi i \mathbf{a}\cdot\mathbf{S}}. \qquad (14.2)$$

For convenience, let us put $2\pi \mathbf{a}\cdot\mathbf{S} = K$, so that expression *14.2* becomes

$$\frac{1 - \exp iMK}{1 - \exp iK}$$

$$= \frac{\exp \frac{1}{2}iMK}{\exp \frac{1}{2}K} \left[\frac{\exp \{-\frac{1}{2}iMK\} - \exp \{\frac{1}{2}iMK\}}{\exp \{-\frac{1}{2}iK\} - \exp \{\frac{1}{2}iK\}} \right].$$

Thus $$G_T(S) = G_0(S) \left[\exp \tfrac{1}{2}i(M-1)K\, \frac{\sin \frac{1}{2}MK}{\sin \frac{1}{2}K} \right]. \qquad (14.3)$$

The diffraction pattern for the whole row is the diffraction pattern of one unit multiplied by the function in the square bracket.

The exponential term is trivial; it has unit modulus and so does not affect the intensity of scattering. It arises only because the origin has been taken at one end of the row of molecules and not in the middle. The rest of the expression is more important; it is

$$\frac{\sin M\pi \mathbf{a}\cdot\mathbf{S}}{\sin \pi \mathbf{a}\cdot\mathbf{S}} \qquad (14.4)$$

− an expression that arises frequently in diffraction-grating problems;

14

its numerator and denominator are both of the order of unity and so the quotient is generally of this order also. The numerator is zero whenever $\mathbf{M}\mathbf{a}\cdot\mathbf{S}$ is integral and therefore at the corresponding values of S the quotient is zero unless $\mathbf{a}\cdot\mathbf{S}$ is integral also. At such values of S the quotient is M, as we can readily see when $\mathbf{a}\cdot\mathbf{S}$ approaches zero. If M is large, therefore, appreciable radiation is diffracted only when the condition $\mathbf{a}\cdot\mathbf{S} =$ an integer is obeyed.

2. *Diffraction by a crystal.* A crystal consists of groups of atoms arranged regularly in three dimensions; that is, they are arranged on a lattice. Suppose that the primitive translations of this lattice are $\mathbf{a}, \mathbf{b}$ and $\mathbf{c}$. Let us consider first a single row of molecules separated by distances $\mathbf{a}$; as in the previous section there will only be appreciable diffracted radiation when the condition $\mathbf{a}\cdot\mathbf{S} = h$, where h is an integer, is satisfied. Let us now regard this whole row as a single unit which, by successive repetition with a translation $\mathbf{b}$ between each, will produce a plane of the crystal. Diffraction from this plane, by the reasoning of 3.1, will be appreciable only in directions for which $\mathbf{b}\cdot\mathbf{S} = k$, where k is an integer. Thus for the complete plane, scattering is appreciable only when *both* conditions $\mathbf{a}\cdot\mathbf{S} = h$ *and* $\mathbf{b}\cdot\mathbf{S} = k$ are obeyed. Finally, we may consider the crystal as a row of these planes separated by intervals of $\mathbf{c}$ and hence producing appreciable scattering only when $\mathbf{c}\cdot\mathbf{S} = l$ where l is another integer.

Thus for the complete crystal three conditions must be obeyed:

$$\left. \begin{aligned} \mathbf{a}\cdot\mathbf{S} &= h \\ \mathbf{b}\cdot\mathbf{S} &= k \\ \mathbf{c}\cdot\mathbf{S} &= l \end{aligned} \right\} \quad (15.1)$$

where h, k and l are integers and may be positive, negative or zero. The equations are called Laue's equations.

Each Laue equation represents a set of equidistant planes in reciprocal space. This may be seen by considering each integral value separately. The physical meaning of the equation $\mathbf{a}\cdot\mathbf{S} = 0$ is that the projection of S upon $\mathbf{a}$ is zero; in other words the equation is satisfied by any vector S perpendicular to $\mathbf{a}$. The vectors S thus trace out a plane perpendicular to $\mathbf{a}$ passing through the origin. The equation $\mathbf{a}\cdot\mathbf{S} = 1$ represents another similar plane making an intercept $\dfrac{1}{|\mathbf{a}|}$. Thus the equation $\mathbf{a}\cdot\mathbf{S} = h$ represents a set of parallel equidistant planes perpendicular to $\mathbf{a}$ (fig. 16). The other two Laue equations represent two other sets of parallel equidistant planes perpendicular to the axes $\mathbf{b}$ and $\mathbf{c}$ respectively, and the values of S that correspond to diffracted beams are those whose ends lie upon the intersections of the three sets of planes. These intersections form the reciprocal lattice.

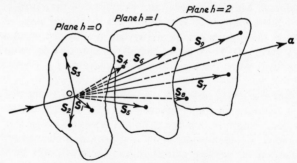

FIG. 16. Physical meaning of the Laue equation $\mathbf{a \cdot S} = h$
Vectors S_1, S_2, S_3 obey $\mathbf{a \cdot S} = 0$
Vectors S_4, S_5, S_6 obey $\mathbf{a \cdot S} = 1$
Vectors S_7, S_8, S_9 obey $\mathbf{a \cdot S} = 2$

In terms of transform theory, Laue's equations imply that the transform of the unit-cell contents is observed only at specific points, denoted by the integers hkl, in reciprocal space. The transform can be regarded as crossed by three sets of sharp planar fringes and only at points where these three sets cross is the transform observed. The underlying transform, as explained in section 2.9, still decides the relative intensities at the points at which it is observed and it is thus customary to consider the transform as 'sampled' (section 1.5) at the points designated by the integers h, k and l, being unobservable elsewhere.

3. *Alternative approach to diffraction by the complete crystal.* One of the attractive features of Fourier-transform methods is that any one result may often be derived in a number of different ways and, in practical applications, this provides a valuable means of checking. The derivation that has just been given of the scattering expression for a complete crystal was chosen because it follows naturally from the earlier sections; there is, however, an alternative approach, making use of two special concepts in Fourier-transform theory that permit a great simplification in the derivation of later results. These concepts – 'folding' or 'convolution' and the 'peak function' – are so important in the development of the Fourier-transform approach that a complete chapter has been devoted to them (Chapter 4), although logically they would be more appropriately discussed here.

4. *Structure factor.* At the sampling points the Fourier transform has values that are known as the *structure factors* of the diffracted beams. Now we require the values of expression 9.3 when Laue's

equations (*15*.1) are satisfied. These values are most simply expressed by putting $\mathbf{r}_n$ in the form

$$\mathbf{r}_n = x_n\mathbf{a} + y_n\mathbf{b} + z_n\mathbf{c} \qquad (17.1)$$

where x_n, y_n and z_n are fractional quantities – the *atomic parameters*. Then, if we designate by F the values of G at which Laue's equations are satisfied

$$F = \sum_1^N f_n \exp 2\pi i(x_n\mathbf{a}{\cdot}\mathbf{S} + y_n\mathbf{b}{\cdot}\mathbf{S} + z_n\mathbf{c}{\cdot}\mathbf{S})$$

$$= \sum_1^N f_n \exp 2\pi i(hx_n + ky_n + lz_n)$$

$$= F(hkl), \text{ say.} \qquad (17.2)$$

We can thus see how the structure-factors arise as special values of the transform. For those already familiar with the conventional derivation of the structure-factor equation it may be useful to regard the transform as the structure factor for non-integral indices.

As with the transform, the structure factor has real and imaginary parts, the values depending upon the choice of origin. If we call the parts A and B,

$$A(hkl) = \sum_1^N f_n \cos 2\pi(hx_n + ky_n + lz_n)$$

and

$$B(hkl) = \sum_1^N f_n \sin 2\pi(hx_n + ky_n + lz_n). \qquad (17.3)$$

The modulus is $(A^2 + B^2)^{\frac{1}{2}}$; it can be obtained from experimental observation of the corresponding diffracted intensity. $|F|^2$ may be called the ideal intensity (section 2.3).

5. *Systematic absences.* We have seen in sections 2.8 and 2.9 that, if two or more molecules are placed in certain relative positions, fringes arise, which may be plane or curved. Frequently the unit cell of a crystal contains such a group of molecules and then these fringes impress themselves on the transform of the unit-cell contents and hence on the transform of the

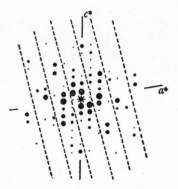

FIG. 17. *h0l*-section of the weighted reciprocal lattice of pyrene with broken lines representing the zero lines of the fringe system

whole crystal. A simple example is given by the diffraction data for pyrene (Hanson, Lipson and Taylor, 1953). For this crystal the fringes can be observed directly from the weighted reciprocal-lattice section (Fig. 17). There is no particular relationship between the fringes and the reciprocal-lattice rows because the molecules do not lie in special positions in the unit cell. It may happen, however, that the fringe zeros coincide with certain reciprocal-lattice rows or planes – for example if the displacement vector between a pair of molecules bears a simple relationship to a crystal-lattice vector.

Suppose, for example, that a crystal has a body-centred lattice; the transform of the unit-cell contents may be regarded as the sum of the transforms of the separate parts $G_0(S')$ separated by a vector $\frac{1}{2}(a+b+c)$ and, from equation 11.2, the resultant is seen to be

$$G_T(S') = G_0(S') \left[1 + \exp \frac{2\pi i}{2} (a+b+c) \cdot S' \right]$$

and, since $a \cdot S' = h$ etc.,

$$G_T(S') = G_0(S')[1 + \exp \pi i(h+k+l)]. \qquad (18.1)$$

That is, the total transform corresponds to the original transform of one molecule, crossed by fringes with zero planes when the sum $(h+k+l)$ is odd.

The characteristic absences for a body-centred lattice are thus seen to be due to the coincidence between reciprocal-lattice planes and zero planes in the fringe system arising when the two transforms are combined.

When two molecules are not parallel more complicated fringe systems occur, but those systems may simplify in certain planes. For example, suppose two molecules are related by an a glide plane perpendicular to the b axis. The transforms of the two molecules are similar but are in orientations related by a plane of symmetry so that, in general, their contributions at any point in reciprocal space are unequal and of different phase. In the plane of symmetry, however, the two must be equal in magnitude, but there will be phase differences depending upon the relative positions of the molecules. For certain values of h, k and l the two transforms exactly cancel and so systematic absences result.

We can see how these absences arise by considering again a molecule with a transform $G_0(S)$. To express the symmetry relationship we must express S in coordinates, say (x^*, y^*, z^*), and if the glide-plane-related molecule has a transform $G_1(S)$

$$G_0(x^*, y^*, z^*) = G_1(x^*, \bar{y}^*, z^*). \qquad (18.2)$$

The equivalent points of the a glide plane are (x, y, z) and $(\frac{1}{2} + x, \bar{y}, z)$, and thus the two molecules are separated by a distance $(\frac{1}{2}, 2\bar{y}, 0)$. The total transform is thus given by the equation

$$G_T(x^*y^*z^*) = G_0(x^*y^*z^*) + G_1(x^*y^*z^*) \exp 2\pi i(\tfrac{1}{2}h - 2ky), \quad (19.1)$$

the exponential term arising in the same way as for equation 18.1. Now, however, it contains a variable y, and so the expression is complicated. If, however, we confine ourselves to the plane of symmetry, $y^* = 0$ and $k = 0$, and thus, making use of the relationship 11.2, we have

$$G_T(x^*0\,z^*) = G_0(x^*0\,z^*)\,[1 + \exp \pi ih]. \quad (19.2)$$

This is zero when h is odd, giving the well-known systematic absences.

To summarize, we can see that systematic absences occur when plane fringes exist throughout reciprocal space (for centred lattices), and when curved fringes have straight intersections with certain planes (for glide planes). By a simple extension of the theory, it can be seen that systematic absences also arise when curved fringes intersect certain lines at regular intervals (for screw axes).

6. *Differences between symmetry of transform of unit-cell contents and transform of whole crystal.* An important point to be noticed, particularly in practical transform work, is that the symmetry of the transform of the unit-cell contents may be lower than that of the complete crystal. The difference arises only when translational symmetry elements are present.

For example, a section of the reciprocal lattice corresponding to a projection of a structure having a two-dimensional space group *pgg* shows two mirror planes. In the transform of the unit cell contents, however, the only symmetry present is a two-fold axis. The transform of the unit cell contents is, however, crossed by curved fringes which are arranged in such a way that the magnitudes at points corresponding to reciprocal-lattice points show the two planes of symmetry.

CHAPTER 4

CONVOLUTION AND THE PEAK FUNCTION

1. *Introduction.* At the end of Chapter 2 a list of corresponding operations in real and reciprocal space was given, and the present chapter is devoted to a detailed treatment of some of these operations. Most of them, such as rotation and translation, are quite familiar and so present little difficulty: the operation corresponding to multiplication is, however, less well known; it is called 'convolution' or 'folding'. It is fully treated in several mathematical works (e.g. Titchmarsh, 1948) but there do not seem to be any specifically physical treatments available. It is the intention in the present chapter to concentrate on the physical significance with only the essential minimum of mathematical justification.

2. *How convolution arises.* For the purposes of the present treatment the concept of convolution arises in answering the question 'What is the result in real or reciprocal space when two functions are multiplied together in the other space?'. By multiplication of two functions we mean that the ordinates of the two functions at a specific point are multiplied together; for example, we may regard a finite crystal as the product of an infinite crystal and a function which is unity everywhere within the boundary of the crystal and zero outside. The problem of diffraction by a finite crystal can then be considered in two separate steps.

Each of the functions in real space has a transform in reciprocal space. The transform of the product is said to be the convolution of the two transforms. Conversely, if two functions are convoluted in one space, the result in the other space is the product of the two transforms. This is known as the 'convolution theorem'; multiplication and convolution are said to be corresponding operations.

Multiplication is, of course, a familiar concept, but convolution is not. Nevertheless convolution is quite common, but often passes unrecognised; it is essentially a mathematical device for reproducing a function at one or more different positions.

A simple example may make it more clear. In considering the action of a diffraction grating, it is usual to consider the diffraction pattern (fig. 21) as the product of two functions, one representing the diffraction pattern of a single element and the other the diffraction pattern of a grating of ideal points. There are several ways of arriving at this result, but on the basis of the concepts to be used in this chapter, we should regard the grating as the convolution of the single element with the spacing represented by the set of ideal points. In other words, the process of convolution turns the single

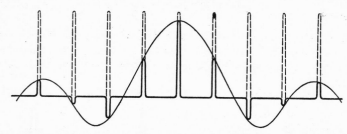

FIG. 21. The relationship between the amplitudes of orders of diffraction from a grating with slits of infinitesimal width (dotted line), the diffraction pattern of a single wider slit (full line) and the diffraction pattern of a grating with wider slits (bolder full line)

element into a set of equally spaced elements. The result already stated – that the diffraction pattern is the product of the transforms of the single element and the ideal point grating – would then be obtained directly from the convolution theorem.

3. *Mathematical treatment.* Let us suppose that we have two functions $\rho(\mathbf{r})$ and $\sigma(\mathbf{r})$ in real space and that their transforms in reciprocal space are $G_\rho(\mathbf{S})$ and $G_\sigma(\mathbf{S})$ respectively. We shall now investigate the result in real space corresponding to the multiplication of these transforms in reciprocal space.

The Fourier transform of the product of $G_\rho(\mathbf{S})$ and $G_\sigma(\mathbf{S})$ is

$$\int G_\rho \cdot G_\sigma(\mathbf{S}) \exp \{2\pi i \mathbf{r} \cdot \mathbf{S}\} \, dV_\mathbf{S}. \qquad (21.1)$$

But $G_\rho(\mathbf{S}) = \int \rho(\mathbf{r}') \exp \{-2\pi i \mathbf{r}' \cdot \mathbf{S}\} \, dV_{\mathbf{r}'}$ where $\mathbf{r}'$ is a vector in

real space which is independent of $\mathbf{r}$. The negative sign occurs because transformation is proceeding in the opposite direction from that in 21.1.

Thus expression 21.1 may be written

$$\int G_\sigma(\mathbf{S}) \left[\int \rho(\mathbf{r}') \exp \left\{ -2\pi i \mathbf{r}' \cdot \mathbf{S} \right\} dV_{\mathbf{r}'} \right] \exp \left\{ 2\pi i \mathbf{r} \cdot \mathbf{S} \right\} dV_\mathbf{S}$$

$$= \int \rho(\mathbf{r}') \left[\int G_\sigma(\mathbf{S}) \exp \left\{ 2\pi i (\mathbf{r} - \mathbf{r}') \cdot \mathbf{S} \right\} dV_\mathbf{S} \right] dV_{\mathbf{r}'}$$

$$= \int \rho(\mathbf{r}') \cdot \sigma(\mathbf{r} - \mathbf{r}') \, dV_{\mathbf{r}'}. \qquad (21.2)$$

This must then be the operation already designated convolution and it is written (Ewald, 1940)

$$\widehat{\rho\sigma}(\mathbf{r}) = \int \rho(\mathbf{r}') \cdot \sigma(\mathbf{r} - \mathbf{r}') \, dV_{\mathbf{r}'} \qquad (22.1)$$

4. *Physical interpretation.* Let us consider the two one-dimensional functions shown in figure 22(i)*a* and *b*. To integrate $\rho(\mathbf{r}')$ from first principles we should divide the area under the curve into small

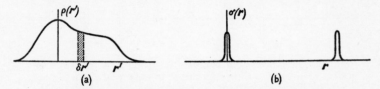

FIG. 22(i). (*a*) The function $\rho(\mathbf{r}')$. (*b*) The function $\sigma(\mathbf{r})$

elements of width $\delta r'$ (fig. 22(i)*a*) and add the areas. Expression 22.1 shows that in order to find the convolution each element of $\rho(\mathbf{r}')$ must be multiplied by $\sigma(\mathbf{r} - \mathbf{r}')$ before integration. Now $\sigma(\mathbf{r} - \mathbf{r}')$ is simply $\sigma(\mathbf{r})$ with its origin moved from $\mathbf{r} = 0$ to $\mathbf{r} = \mathbf{r}'$. The final convolution is thus obtained by placing the origin of function

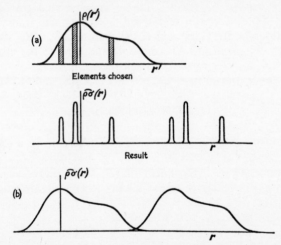

FIG. 22(ii). (*a*) The convolution operation for three elements of $\rho(\mathbf{r}')$ only. (*b*) The complete convolution operation

$\sigma(\mathbf{r})$ successively at the centres of all the elementary strips of $\rho(\mathbf{r}')$, each time multiplying by the value of $\rho(\mathbf{r}')$, and then adding up all the ordinates. Fig. 22(ii)*a* shows this operation for three elements and fig. 22(ii)*b* the completed operation.

5. *Physical significance of converse.* Let us suppose that we wish to find the transform of this convolution. We have seen that the convolution was obtained by placing $\sigma(\mathbf{r})$ with its origin at $\mathbf{r}'$, multiplying by $\rho(\mathbf{r}')$ and adding for all values of $\mathbf{r}'$ for which $\rho(\mathbf{r}')$ is non-zero. The transform will be the sum (section 2.8) of the transforms of all these elements.

The transform of one element is $G_\sigma(\mathbf{S}) \times \rho(\mathbf{r}')$ and since its origin is at $\mathbf{r}'$ its phase, relative to the true origin, is given by $\exp 2\pi i\mathbf{r}'\cdot\mathbf{S}$ and the total transform is $\Sigma G_\sigma(\mathbf{S}) \times \rho(\mathbf{r}') \exp 2\pi i\mathbf{r}'\cdot\mathbf{S}$ or, proceeding to the limit,

$$\int G_\sigma(\mathbf{S})\rho(\mathbf{r}') \exp 2\pi i\mathbf{r}'\cdot\mathbf{S}\, dV_{\mathbf{r}'}$$

$$= G_\sigma(\mathbf{S}) \int \rho(\mathbf{r}') \exp 2\pi i\mathbf{r}'\cdot\mathbf{S}\, dV_{\mathbf{r}'}$$

$$= G_\sigma G_\rho(\mathbf{S}) \qquad (23.1)$$

i.e. the transform of the convolution is thus the product of the individual transforms.†

6. *The Peak Function.* Some of the applications to be discussed in chapters 6 and 7 involve the use of the convolution theorem just developed in its most general form. For many applications, however, a simplification arises if use is made of the peak function (cf. delta function; e.g. Jaeger, 1949).

Let us consider for the moment the example already cited of the simple diffraction grating. In studying this problem from the standpoint of the convolution concept it is necessary to find two functions, one of which represents the periodicity of the grating and the other the width of each element. The function representing width can easily be found; it is simply a step function having a value of zero outside certain limits and a finite constant value between the limits. The function representing periodicity is more difficult. Ideally this

† A more formal but not completely rigorous treatment is given below:

$$G_{\widehat{\rho\sigma}}(\mathbf{S}) = \int \widehat{\rho\sigma}(r) \exp 2\pi i\mathbf{r}\cdot\mathbf{S}\, dV_{\mathbf{r}}$$

$$= \int \left[\int \rho(\mathbf{r}')\, \sigma(\mathbf{r} - \mathbf{r}')\, dV_{\mathbf{r}'}\right] \exp 2\pi i\mathbf{r}\cdot\mathbf{S}\, dV_{\mathbf{r}}$$

$$= \int \rho(\mathbf{r}') \left[\int \sigma(\mathbf{r} - \mathbf{r}') \exp 2\pi i\mathbf{r}\cdot\mathbf{S}\, dV_{\mathbf{r}}\right] dV_{\mathbf{r}'}.$$

Now put $\mathbf{u} = \mathbf{r} - \mathbf{r}'$.

Then $\quad G_{\widehat{\rho\sigma}}(\mathbf{S}) = \int \rho(\mathbf{r}') \exp 2\pi i\mathbf{r}'\cdot\mathbf{S}\, dV_{\mathbf{r}'} \int \sigma(\mathbf{u}) \exp 2\pi i\mathbf{u}\cdot\mathbf{S}\, dV_{\mathbf{r}'}.$

$\mathbf{u}$ and $\mathbf{r}$ are independent variables in the same space; therefore $G_{\widehat{\rho\sigma}}(\mathbf{S}) = G_\sigma G_\rho(\mathbf{S})$ as obtained before.

function represents a grating with the same periodicity as the grating under consideration but with slits of infinitesimal width. In spite of the infinitesimal width, however, they must transmit a *finite* amount of light. These properties can be realized in principle by considering first a grating of the right periodicity and with slits of finite width and finite length. Then, while the area of each slit is kept constant, the width is decreased and the length increased. In the limit the width is infinitesimal but the area, and hence the transmission, is still finite.

This same procedure is adopted in three-dimensional problems. A function is required such that it is zero everywhere except at certain points and at these precise points it is infinite – but to such an order that the volume integral is finite. It can be approached by starting with some function with a finite peak width and allowing it to shrink while keeping the volume integral constant. Such a function is called a Peak Function. If the integrated value at the points defined by vectors $\mathbf{r}_n$ is m then it is written (Ewald, 1940)

$$Z_{\mathbf{r}_n}^m. \tag{24.1}$$

It is not necessary for the purposes of this monograph to investigate its precise mathematical form or its derivation.

7. *Applications.* Let us now consider how the concepts of convolution and the peak function may be used in practical crystallographic problems. Consider a two-dimensional function $\rho(\mathbf{r})$ which has a magnitude d within a circle of radius a centred at the origin of real space, and zero everywhere outside this circle. Let us find the convolution of this function with a peak function $Z_{\mathbf{r}_1}^1$ – a function

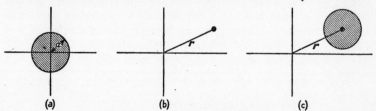

(a)   (b)   (c)

FIG. 24. (*a*) A function $\rho(\mathbf{r})$. (*b*) A peak function at a position $\mathbf{r}$. (*c*) The convolution of 4(*a*) and 4(*b*)

which is, by definition, zero everywhere except at $\mathbf{r}_1$ where it is infinite to such an order that the integrated value is 1. The problem is illustrated in fig. 24*a* and *b*.

The convolution, from equation 22.1, is

$$\widehat{\rho Z_{\mathbf{r}_1}^1}(\mathbf{r}) = \int \rho(\mathbf{r}') Z_{\mathbf{r}_1}^1(\mathbf{r} - \mathbf{r}') \, dV_{\mathbf{r}'}. \tag{24.2}$$

Now $Z^1_{r_1}(\mathbf{r}-\mathbf{r}')$ can be non-zero *only* when $\mathbf{r}-\mathbf{r}'=\mathbf{r}_1$ by definition, i.e. R.H.S. is always zero unless $\mathbf{r}'=\mathbf{r}-\mathbf{r}_1$.

Then

$$\rho\widehat{Z_{r_1}}(\mathbf{r}) = \int \rho(\mathbf{r}-\mathbf{r}_1)Z^1_{r_1}(\mathbf{r}_1)\,dV_{\mathbf{r}'}. \qquad (25.1)$$

At any particular value of $\mathbf{r}$ at which the convolution is required $\rho(\mathbf{r}-\mathbf{r}_1)$ is constant and thus the convolution is

$$\rho(\mathbf{r}-\mathbf{r}_1)\int Z^1_{r_1}(\mathbf{r}_1)\,dV_{\mathbf{r}'} = \rho(\mathbf{r}-\mathbf{r}_1) \qquad (25.2)$$

by definition of $Z^1_{r_1}$. In other words, the convolution is simply the function $\rho(\mathbf{r})$ with its origin translated to $\mathbf{r}_1$ (fig. 24c).

Consider now a peak function $Z^1_{r_n}$ which is zero everywhere except at the ends of a set of vectors $\mathbf{r}_n$ where it is infinite to such an order

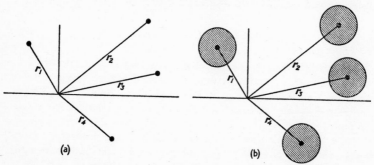

(a)   (b)

FIG. 25. (a) The vectors $\mathbf{r}_n$. (b) The convolution of 24a and 25a

that the integral over a small range including the point is unity (fig. 25a). Let us consider the convolution of a function $\rho(\mathbf{r})$, as in the previous example, with $Z^1_{r_n}$. As before $\rho\widehat{Z^1_{r_n}}(\mathbf{r}) = \int \rho(\mathbf{r}')Z^1_{r_n}(\mathbf{r}-\mathbf{r}')\,dV_{\mathbf{r}'}$, but now $Z^1_{r_n}(\mathbf{r}-\mathbf{r}')$ is non-zero only at a series of points $\mathbf{r}-\mathbf{r}'=\mathbf{r}_n$ and as the integration is over all space, the total is the sum of the various peak integrations, each of which is $1 \times \rho(\mathbf{r}') = \rho(\mathbf{r}-\mathbf{r}_n)$.

$$\rho\widehat{Z_{r_n}}(\mathbf{r}) = \Sigma\rho(\mathbf{r}-\mathbf{r}_n) \qquad (25.3)$$

But $\Sigma\rho(\mathbf{r}-\mathbf{r}_n)$ is simply the old function at *each* of the points $\mathbf{r}_n$ and, where overlapping occurs, the sum taken (fig. 25b). Thus the molecule whose transform is discussed in section 2.5 could be regarded as the convolution of the transform of each *atom* with a peak function representing the atomic centres. The transform of the molecule is the product of the transform of the atom $f_n(\mathbf{S})$ with the transform of the peak function. The transform of the peak function is

$$\int Z^1_{r_n} \exp 2\pi i \mathbf{r} \cdot \mathbf{S} \, d\mathbf{V_r} = \sum \exp 2\pi i \mathbf{r}_n \cdot \mathbf{S}.$$

Thus the total transform $= f_n(\mathbf{S}) \sum \exp 2\pi i \mathbf{r}_n \cdot \mathbf{S}$ as before (cf. 9.2).

8. *Alternative derivation of the transform of a complete crystal* (see 3.3). A perfect crystal consists of a particular atomic arrangement repeated identically at the points of a regular lattice. In terms of the concepts of the present chapter it may therefore be represented as the convolution of the atomic arrangement with a peak function of unit content defining the lattice. In the last section we found the transform of a peak function $Z^1_{r_n}$ which was zero everywhere except at the ends of a set of vectors $\mathbf{r}_n$. This function will serve to define the crystal lattice but, as the ends of the set of vectors will now lie on a lattice, we will use the symbol $\mathbf{r}_l$ to denote them and the peak function will be $Z^1_{r_l}$. The transform of this peak function is

$$\int Z^1_{r_l} \exp 2\pi i \mathbf{r} \cdot \mathbf{S} \, d\mathbf{V_r} = \sum \exp 2\pi i \mathbf{r}_l \cdot \mathbf{S}. \qquad (26.1)$$

Now $\exp 2\pi i \mathbf{r}_l \cdot \mathbf{S}$ is a quantity which oscillates continuously as $\mathbf{S}$ and $\mathbf{r}_e$ change. At any particular value of $\mathbf{S}$ the average value (if there is a sufficiently large number of lattice points) will be zero unless $\mathbf{r}_l \cdot \mathbf{S}$ is integral and remains integral as $\mathbf{r}_l$ changes from point to point.

Now $\mathbf{r} = u\mathbf{a} + v\mathbf{b} + w\mathbf{c}$ where u, v and w are integers. Hence $u\mathbf{a} \cdot \mathbf{S} + v\mathbf{b} \cdot \mathbf{S} + w\mathbf{c} \cdot \mathbf{S}$ must remain integral as u, v, w change by unity; hence $\mathbf{a} \cdot \mathbf{S}$, $\mathbf{b} \cdot \mathbf{S}$ and $\mathbf{c} \cdot \mathbf{S}$ must each be integral. That is

$$\left. \begin{array}{l} \mathbf{a} \cdot \mathbf{S} = h \\ \mathbf{b} \cdot \mathbf{S} = k \\ \mathbf{c} \cdot \mathbf{S} = l \end{array} \right\} \qquad (26.2)$$

which are the Laue equations (15.1) again. The transform of the peak function representing the crystal lattice is thus zero everywhere except at certain points with values of $\mathbf{S}$ given by these equations. A proof that these points also lie on a lattice – the reciprocal lattice – has already been given in section 3.2. At these points the transform has a peak value which depends on the number of real lattice points which have been included in the summation – that is, on the size of the crystal. In other words the transform of the peak function representing the crystal lattice is another peak function zero everywhere except at the points of the reciprocal lattice.

The transform of the complete crystal may now be obtained by application of the convolution theorem; it is the product of the transform of one unit cell with the transform of the peak function representing the lattice. That is, it is zero everywhere except at the points of the reciprocal lattice and there it is the product of the transform of the unit cell at that point and the amplitude of the reciprocal lattice peak function, which is the same at all points and depends on the size of the crystal.

This way of looking at diffraction by a crystal is particularly important for the study of finite and imperfect crystals (see Chapter 7) and for the study of Fourier synthesis (see Chapter 6).

CHAPTER 5

GEOMETRY OF DIFFRACTION

1 *Limiting sphere.* It is useful at this stage to consider further properties of the vector S which was introduced in section 2.2 and which defines the space in which the Fourier transform exists. S is defined as $s - s_0$ where s_0 and s are vectors of modulus $\frac{1}{\lambda}$ in the direction of the incident and diffracted waves respectively. As s_0 and s take up different directions in space, S also takes up different directions but it may also vary in modulus from zero when s_0 and s are in the

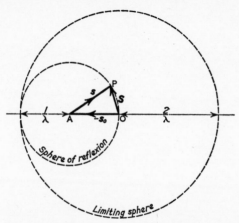

FIG. 28. The relationship between the reciprocal vectors, the sphere of reflexion and the limiting sphere

same direction to $\frac{2}{\lambda}$ when they are in opposite directions. The end of the vector S (fig. 28) may thus occupy any point within a sphere of radius $\frac{2}{\lambda}$ – the limiting sphere, as it is called (Bernal, 1926).

The limiting sphere determines the extent of a Fourier transform that can be observed with radiation of a given wavelength. The Fourier transform was introduced as a function giving, in amplitude and phase, the scattered radiation associated with specific values of S; we can thus imagine the transform as a solid object – which we shall refer to as the reciprocal solid – in which each point is associated with a density of matter (reciprocal matter!) corresponding to the modulus of the transform at that point, the nature of the matter being such that it changes the phase of the radiation by an amount corresponding to the phase of the transform at that point.

It will be remembered that the moduli of s_0 and s were taken as $\frac{1}{\lambda}$ in order to make the Fourier transform independent of λ (section 1.3). Thus the transform is invariant and, in principle, of infinite extent. However, the amount of the transform that can be explored with a given wavelength is limited to that falling within the limiting sphere. Since this sphere has radius $\frac{2}{\lambda}$ we can see that in order to map the whole of the transform we should need a radiation of vanishingly small wavelength, and that the longer the wavelength the smaller the extent of the transform that can be explored. From the reciprocal relationship between an object and its transform we know that the smallest details in the object correspond to the outermost parts of the transform; therefore in order to explore the fine detail of an object we must use as small a wavelength as possible in order that the limiting sphere should be as large as possible.

2. *Sphere of reflexion.* We must now consider the more practical matters of the observation of the reciprocal solid. Let us suppose that the radiation is incident in a direction AO on an object placed at A (fig. 28). The line OA represents the vector $-s_0$ and the line AP represents the vector s for a particular direction of observation. The line OP is then the vector S.

If the object is fixed (so that its transform is fixed) and AO is a fixed direction, then the free end of S must lie on the surface of a sphere with its centre at A and with a radius $\frac{1}{\lambda}$. This sphere is known as the sphere of reflexion. Only those parts of the reciprocal solid that lie on the surface of this sphere can be observed for a given incident-beam direction relative to the object.

If the wavelength of the radiation is small compared with the detail in the object we are examining, then the sphere of reflexion is very large and the part that intersects the reciprocal solid approximates to a plane passing through the origin and thus for any one setting of the object we can explore a plane section of the reciprocal solid. Electron diffraction provides an example; with a wavelength of 0·05 Å sections of the diffraction pattern of a single crystal can be observed (e.g. Cowley, 1953a).

If, however, the radiation has a wavelength which is of the same order of magnitude as the detail in which we are interested – as, for example, when we use X-rays of wavelength 1·5 Å to investigate interatomic distances – the sphere of reflexion may lie completely inside the relevant part of the reciprocal solid. The geometry of the observations is then rather complicated. Before taking the subject further however, we must consider another complication – the nature of the diffraction patterns of crystals, which are the most usual diffracting objects for X-rays.

3. *Reciprocal lattice.* In section **4**.8 we saw that the Fourier transform of a crystal is a lattice peak function – that is, it is zero everywhere except at mathematical points arranged on a lattice. The reciprocal solid mentioned in the last section is thus a set of regularly spaced lattice points – the reciprocal lattice – having no finite extent (for an unbounded crystal) but associated with definite amplitudes and phases. We can see then that the amount of information collected by the sphere of reflexion is very small indeed; for perfect experimental conditions and a perfect crystal the chance that a reciprocal-lattice point lies on the sphere of reflexion is vanishingly small and thus no diffracted beams are produced.

This fact has been predominant in the designing of X-ray diffracto-meters. In the first method – the Laue method – use is made of the white radiation from an X-ray tube; then the sphere of reflexion is broadened because it is connected with a range in λ (fig. 30) and so a number of reciprocal-lattice points can lie on it. This method was, of course, that used by Fried-rich, Knipping and Laue (1912) in discovering X-ray diffraction. It is now of little importance because each diffracted beam is produced by a different wave-length.

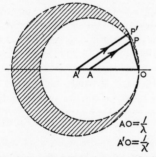

$AO = \frac{1}{\lambda}$

$A'O = \frac{1}{\lambda'}$

FIG. 30. The broadening of the sphere of reflexion when a range λ to λ' of wavelengths is used

All the methods used in practice involve rotating the crystal so that reciprocal-lattice points move successively through the surface of the sphere of reflexion. The latest devices to be developed (e.g. Buerger, 1944) arrange for the film to be moved also, in such a way that the sphere of reflexion rolls tangentially to it; then a complete undistorted representation of a section of the reciprocal lattice is obtained.

It is interesting to note that, if a crystal with a large unit cell and thus a fine reciprocal lattice is used, the sphere of reflexion near the centre of reciprocal space approximates to a plane with respect to the reciprocal lattice. It is then possible to see an approximate representation of the reciprocal lattice near the centre of an ordinary oscillation X-ray photograph.

4. *Reciprocal-lattice constants.* The reciprocal lattice has constants that are conventionally given the symbols a^*, b^* and c^*. (It is perhaps unfortunate that this designation is used because it is also used for representing complex conjugates; but it is so well established that it would be futile to try to change it.) The values of S corresponding to diffraction conditions are then given by the equation

$$S(hkl) = ha^* + kb^* + lc^*. \qquad (31.1)$$

The first Laue equation can then be written as

$$ha \cdot a^* + ka \cdot b^* + la \cdot c^* = h. \qquad (31.2)$$

But **a** is perpendicular to b^* and c^* and thus $a \cdot b^*$ and $a \cdot c^*$ are zero.

$$\therefore a \cdot a^* = 1. \qquad (31.3)$$

This simple relationship is not however particularly useful for evaluating a^* generally, because the angle between **a** and a^* is a complicated function of the unit-cell dimensions. If it so happens that **a** and a^* are in the same direction – as they are, for example in an orthorhombic crystal – then $|a^*| = \dfrac{1}{|a|}$.

For a general (triclinic) unit cell it is best to make use of the expression for the volume of the unit cell

$$V = a \cdot b \times c. \qquad (31.4)$$

Then
$$\frac{a \cdot b \times c}{V} = 1. \qquad (31.5)$$

Comparing this equation with *31.*3 we see that

$$a^* = \frac{b \times c}{V}. \qquad (31.6)$$

This expression and the symmetrically related ones for b^* and c^* can be evaluated in terms of the unit-cell constants.

5. *Relationship to Bragg's law.* It will be noted that section **5.**2 is entitled 'sphere of reflexion' despite any apparent connexion with the phenomenon of reflexion itself. The reason for the name is, of course, that it arose from the basic idea of Bragg (1913) that the diffracted beams from a crystal could be interpreted as reflexions from lattice planes; this idea has been so fruitful that any new theoretical approach would be incomplete if it were not shown to be simply related to the reflexion concept.

We must first show that the vector S is perpendicular to a lattice plane. We may define any plane in terms of a vector **r** from the origin to any point in the plane, and it is easy to see that the equation

$$\mathbf{r} \cdot \mathbf{S} = 1 \qquad (32.1)$$

is a plane to which $\mathbf{S}$ is a normal. (The projection of $\mathbf{r}$ upon $\mathbf{S}$ is constant, which, as we can see from fig. 32, is true only if $\mathbf{S}$ is normal to the plane). Now the first Laue equation can be put in the form

$$(\mathbf{a}/h) \cdot \mathbf{S} = 1 \qquad (32.2)$$

and thus the vector $\mathbf{a}/h$ is one value of $\mathbf{r}$, ($\mathbf{r}_3$ in fig. 32). In other words the plane 32.1 makes an intercept $\mathbf{a}/h$ on the x axis. Similarly from

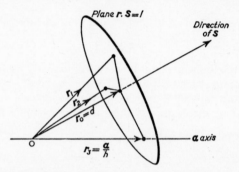

FIG. 32. The projection of $\mathbf{r}_n$ upon $\mathbf{S}$ is constant only if $\mathbf{S}$ is normal to plane containing the ends of all the vectors $\mathbf{r}_n$

the other two Laue equations it makes intercepts $\mathbf{b}/k$ and $\mathbf{c}/l$ on the other two axes. Thus the plane is a lattice plane as defined in the elementary text books (e.g. Henry, Lipson and Wooster, 1951), and $\mathbf{S}$ is normal to it.

The spacing d ($\mathbf{r}_0$ in fig. 32) is the scalar product of $\mathbf{r}$ and a unit vector in the direction of $\mathbf{S}$; that is,

$$d = \mathbf{r} \cdot \frac{\mathbf{S}}{|\mathbf{S}|}$$

$$= \frac{1}{|\mathbf{S}|} \text{ from equation } 32.1. \qquad (32.3)$$

But (fig. 3)

$$|\mathbf{S}| = \frac{2 \sin \theta}{\lambda}. \qquad (32.4)$$

Thus

$$2d \sin \theta = \lambda. \qquad (32.5)$$

This is the well-known Bragg equation.

Moreover we see from fig. 33 that $\mathbf{s}_0$ and $\mathbf{s}$ have the same relationship as the incident and reflected beams with respect to a mirror, and it is for this reason that the term reflexion is so widely used.

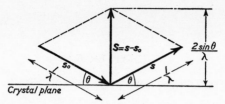

FIG. 33. The vectors s and s_0 are related to the vector S as the incident and reflected waves are related to the normal in regular reflexion from a plane

But it should be noted that 'reflexion' occurs only when the extra condition imposed by Bragg's equation is obeyed and so it is essentially different from ordinary reflexion.

CHAPTER 6

RECOMBINATION OF THE SCATTERED WAVES

1. *Introduction.* In section **1.**1 it was stated that an image of an object may be constructed if the angular distribution of intensity, frequency and phase of the scattered radiation is known. In terms of the Fourier-transform concept this is simply the statement that, if the Fourier transform of an object is completely determined, the object also is completely determined and its form may be obtained by Fourier transformation. The phase for X-rays cannot be measured experimentally and in consequence the direct production of an image of a crystal structure by Fourier transformation of the diffraction pattern is not, in general, possible.

There are several more-or-less indirect ways of determining the phases for certain kinds of structure and thence producing an image by Fourier transformation; the process is usually called Fourier synthesis when operated from reciprocal space to real space. For example, if the structure contains a single heavy atom at a centre of symmetry, the contribution that it makes may be regarded as positive throughout the limiting sphere of reciprocal space and may be sufficiently large to make the total contribution for all atoms in the unit cell positive everywhere (e.g. platinum phthalocyanine; Robertson and Woodward, 1940). Phases may sometimes be deduced by comparing the diffraction patterns of members of an isomorphous series in which a particular atom is replaced successively by atoms of different atomic number (e.g. strychnine sulphate and selenate; Bokhoven, Schoone and Bijvoet, 1951). More recently a number of methods based on mathematical relationships between the phases of reflexions have been developed (see 7.4.2). However, in this chapter, we are more concerned with the problem of producing an image when these methods are not available.

2. *The Patterson or '*$|F|^2$*' synthesis.* Since the intensities are recorded without information about phase it is natural to investigate the result of transforming the intensity distribution (Patterson, 1934). The intensity at any point in reciprocal space is proportional to the product $G(S) \cdot G^*(S)$ (section **2.**3). The transform of this product is, by the convolution theorem of **4.**3, the convolution of the transform of $G(S)$ – which is the electron density – with the transform of $G^*(S)$ – which is the electron density inverted in the origin. Thus the transformation operation applied to the intensities alone produces an image of the electron density convoluted with the electron density inverted in the origin. At first sight, this would appear to be almost as useful as an image of electron density itself, but further investigation shows that the unravelling of the two convoluted functions is not, in general, an easy process.

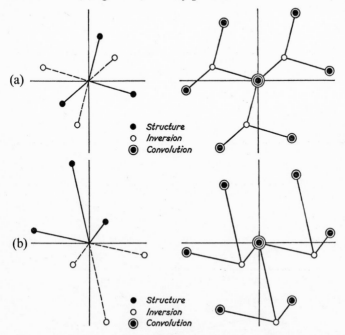

FIG. 35. (a) Convolution of a simple structure with its own inversion. (b) Convolution of the same structure with its inversion in an origin different from that of 35a; the final result is the same

Figure 35a illustrates the convolution of a simple structure of three atoms with its own inversion. It was prepared by drawing the structure three times with its centre of inversion placed successively at the three atomic centres of the inverted structure. The most obvious feature is that the position of the origin of the initial unit cell has no effect; figure 35b is the same structure with a different origin and it may be seen that the resulting convolution is identical with that of 35a. This result would, of course, be expected since the position of an object relative to the chosen origin governs the phase of the scattered radiation (section 2.8) and no information about phase has been included.

Clearly a more complicated structure (e.g. fig. 36) would give rise to a much more complicated pattern, possibly involving con-

siderable overlapping and, without previous knowledge of some
details of the structure, the interpretation may be very difficult.
Much attention has, however, been devoted to the problem, and the
experience gained has enabled several fairly complicated structures to
be derived (e.g. Beevers and Robertson, 1950); nevertheless, despite

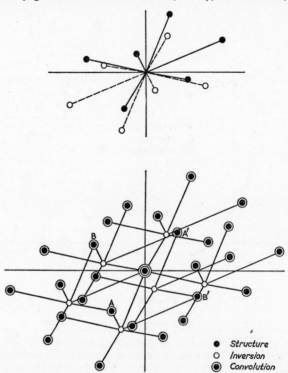

FIG. 36. Convolution of a more complex structure with its own
inversion; some of the points such as A, A', B, B' in the final
convolution overlap

considerable theoretical discussion (e.g. Buerger, 1951) no general
method of solution has so far resulted.

Patterson synthesis is a transformation of X-ray data in reciprocal
space into information in real space. We shall show in section 7.2.3
that the opposite approach – that of interpreting directly the X-ray
data in reciprocal space – is also possible and can sometimes be more
productive.

3. *Fourier synthesis using phases for a trial structure.* When a
structure is being studied by trial-and-error methods and a fair
measure of aggreement has been reached between observed and

calculated intensities, a common procedure is to make a Fourier transformation of the observed intensities combined with the calculated phases for the trial structure. We shall now investigate the result of such a procedure. Let us suppose that the complex quantity representing the Fourier transform of the true structure at a particular point in reciprocal space may be written $|F_0| \exp i\phi_0$,[†] that the corresponding calculated quantity for the proposed structure

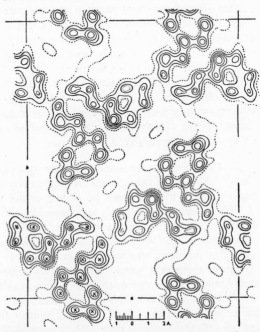

FIG. 37. Fourier synthesis of the c-axis projection of triphenylene based on an incorrect trial structure (Klug, 1950a). The true structure has molecules of the same shape in the same orientation but in different positions in the unit cell (Pinnock, Taylor and Lipson, 1956)

is $|F_c| \exp i\phi_c$. $|F_c|$, ϕ_c are known quantities and $|F_0|$, the observed structure amplitude, is also known. The quantity used in the transformation is

$$|F_0| \exp i\phi_c \qquad (37.1)$$

which may be written

$$\frac{|F_0|}{|F_c|} \cdot |F_c| \exp i\phi_c , \qquad (37.2)$$

[†]Although we have followed the standard practice in X-ray crystallography and have used the symbol $|F_0|$ it should be noted that the modulus signs are really redundant. F_0 is the structure amplitude, a scalar quantity; F_c the structure factor is, of course, a vector quantity and needs the modulus sign if its magnitude only is implied.

that is, it may be regarded as the product of the complete Fourier transform of the proposed structure multiplied by a function having zero phase angle everywhere and an amplitude $\dfrac{|F_0|}{|F_c|}$. Clearly the transformation of this product results in a convolution of the proposed structure with the transform of the function $\dfrac{|F_0|}{|F_c|}$.

Since this latter function has zero phase everywhere, its transform will have a large peak at the origin which in the process of convolution will make the calculated structure predominant. If $|F_0| = |F_c|$ everywhere, then there will *only* be an origin peak and the result is simply the calculated structure which is identical with the true structure. If $|F_0| \neq |F_c|$, then there will be some background which will modify the calculated structure. It is obvious, however, that the predominant tendency is for the process of transformation to give an image which closely resembles the trial structure even though this may not be correct (fig. 37).

4. *Errors due to series termination.* Various discussions (e.g. Bragg and West, 1930) have been made of the errors introduced in performing Fourier synthesis when all orders of diffraction are not included. The effect can most easily be grasped by consideration of the convolution theorem. Let us suppose that all reflexions above a certain value of $\sin \theta$ are to be excluded. This is equivalent to multiplying the function representing the true transform extending throughout reciprocal space by a function which is unity inside a certain limit and zero outside this limit. The resulting transform is clearly the convolution of the true structure with the transform of this limiting function. For example, in two dimensions, the exclusion of reflexions above $\sin \theta = 0.6$ is equivalent to multiplying by a function which is unity inside a circle of radius corresponding to $\sin \theta = 0.6$ and zero outside it. The transform of this is the same as the diffraction pattern of a circular hole – a Bessel function having a central maximum surrounded by diffraction rings. The final sythesis then, is the convolution of the structure with this Bessel function; that is, all the atoms appear to be surrounded by diffraction rings.

Similarly, if, because of anisotropic temperature effects, the limit of observable reflexions is not a sphere but a spheroid, the atoms will no longer be spherical in the image but will have a shape corresponding to the transform of the spheroid. The result is, in fact, exactly comparable with that of the finite crystal (see Chapter 7) except that here the limitation is in reciprocal space and the effects are in real space: for the finite crystal, the limitation is in real space and the effects are in reciprocal space.

APPLICATIONS OF
FOURIER TRANSFORM THEORY

1. *Introduction.* Although our main aim has been to describe the Fourier transform approach to the *teaching* of X-ray diffraction, we are aware that there are many people – including ourselves – for whom a particular form of presentation becomes real, and worth teaching, only if it can be shown to have practical advantages as well as theoretical elegance. We therefore propose, in this final chapter, to show how the transform approach may be used in practical problems. It is obviously impossible to give an exhaustive treatment here and the illustrations have been chosen, as far as possible, to indicate the diversity of the problems in which applications may be found. They have been divided into three groups. First, a few of the recent techniques used in structure determination that have been developed by direct application of Fourier-transform theory are described. Then follows an account of some of the problems of finite and imperfect structures in which the explicit use of Fourier transform theory is almost essential. Finally one or two of the modern mathematical approaches to crystal-structure problems are shown to be capable of qualitative physical description in terms of Fourier transforms.

The Fourier transform may thus be regarded as a unifying concept, drawing together the apparently diverse sections of the subject of X-ray diffraction and emphasizing their essential relationships.

2. *New techniques.* Several new techniques in crystal-structure determination have emerged from Fourier-transform studies during the past five or six years. They are based primarily on the recognition that the X-ray diffraction pattern is a sample at specific points of the Fourier transform of the contents of a single unit cell, and therefore that the reflexions are not completely separate, independent entities, but may be related in various ways. The use of optical-transform techniques (see Appendix II) has considerably speeded up these developments as it makes possible the rapid production of transforms and hence increases the rate at which experience of transform relationships may be gained. As mentioned in the preface, these techniques will be more fully described elsewhere and in the present section attention is confined to general principles.

2.1. *Test of correctness.* Knott (1940), Klug (1950*b*), Hanson, Lipson and Taylor (1953), and others, have described the advantages of comparing observed X-ray intensities with the transform of the contents of a unit cell rather than with the structure-factors calculated only at reciprocal-lattice points. Comparison of the observed intensities with the structure factors at reciprocal-lattice points tends to give a 'yes-or-no' answer to the question 'Is the trial structure correct?' On the other hand, comparison with the continuous function – because the gradients in the vicinity of reciprocal-lattice points may be seen immediately – tends to answer the question 'Is the trial structure near to the correct solution and in what way must it be changed to improve the agreement?'. This is particularly true for plane molecules for which, from a single calculation of the principal two-dimensional section of the transform, the full three-dimensional structure may be determined. It is true for non-planar molecules as well, and techniques for making better use of transforms for more complex molecules are being developed, (e.g. Morley and Taylor, 1957). In structure determination by trial-and-error methods the problem is to pick out the most promising structure from a number of trial arrangements; comparison of the observed intensities with the continuous function – the Fourier transform – for the trial structures probably permits the recognition of a structure as essentially correct at a stage earlier than would be possible if the comparison were made with the structure factor at reciprocal-lattice points only.

2.2. *Sign determination.* For centro-symmetrical structures, the transform is real (section 2.6) and the amplitude passes through zero each time the phase changes from 0 to π. The transform is thus divided into regions of varying height and shape, separated by lines of zero amplitude. Superposition of the reciprocal-lattice section on the transform permits the sign associated with each reciprocal-lattice point to be read immediately, and the effect on the signs of changes in orientation can be seen at once by changing the relative orientation of the reciprocal-lattice section and the transform (Knott, 1940; Pinnock and Taylor, 1955). Again the advantage of having the continuous function available may be seen, since the reliability of the sign may be assessed; signs associated with points lying on very steep slopes are likely to change more readily with slight modifications to the structure than those associated with points lying on plateau-like regions of the transform. Fig. 41 illustrates this for naphthalene (Knott, 1940).

Attempts have been made with varying success to use transforms for phase determination for non-centrosymmetrical structures (Hanson *et al*, 1953).

2.3. *Direct recognition of molecular features.* In section 7.2.2, mention was made of the division of the transform of a centro-symmetrical object into regions separated by lines of zero amplitude. For the transform of the contents of a complete unit cell of a structure,

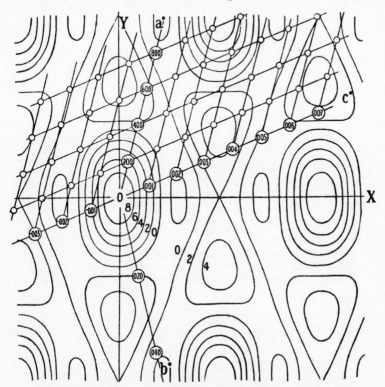

FIG. 41. Calculated transform for naphthalene with the correctly oriented reciprocal lattice superimposed. 202 and 801 are examples of reflexions which are sensitive to small changes in orientation; 203 and 802 are comparatively insensitive

although the height and extent of the regions differ in detail from point to point, there is a general 'texture' which is roughly reciprocally related to the overall shape and dimensions of the unit cell contents. For a few simple molecular structures the molecules are sufficiently small for the spaces between them – governed by the van der Waals distances – to be an important fraction of the unit cell. In other words the shape and size of the contents are appreciably different from those of the cell itself. The 'texture' of the transform is then coarser than that of the reciprocal lattice and, in general, several reciprocal-lattice points will lie within each region

D

of the transform. Thus, for durene (Robertson, 1933), the *b*-axis projection has an effective unit cell which contains only one molecule

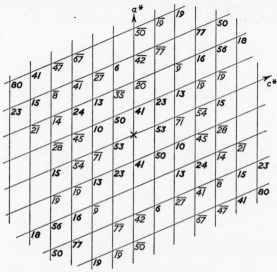

FIG. 42(i). A reciprocal-lattice section for durene showing approximate unitary structure factors combined with the signs of the calculated F's; positive values are in bolder type than negative values

FIG. 42(ii). A small portion of a reciprocal-lattice section for purpurogallin showing approximate unitary structure factors combined with the signs of the calculated F's; positive values are in bolder type than negative values. The portion corresponds to the region immediately above the inset molecule in fig. 43. The black discs indicate the weighting as given in fig. 43

with a maximum projected dimension of about 5 Å, which is not much larger than the average van der Waals distance of 3·5 Å. Fig. 42(i) shows the approximate unitary structure factors for durene plotted on the reciprocal-lattice section and combined with the signs of the calculated structure factors. The underlying regions of constant phase in the transform, covering several unit cells of the reciprocal lattice, can easily be seen. For more complex structures with larger unit cells the texture is much finer and the phases of adjacent reflexions are not related in such an obvious way; fig. 42(ii) shows part of a reciprocal-lattice section for purpurogallin (Taylor, 1952a; Hanson et al, 1953) with approximate unitary structure factors and the signs of the calculated structure factors.

A consideration of the rules for the combination of transforms (section 2.10) shows, however, that a small portion of a unit cell – having a correspondingly coarse-textured transform – may give rise

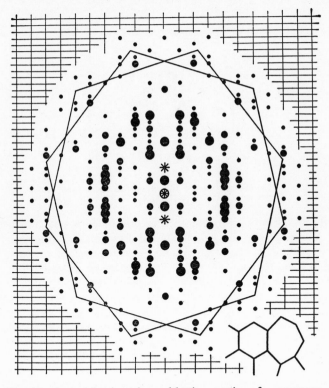

Fig. 43. A weighted reciprocal-lattice section for purpurogallin. The points of the two hexagons lie approximately at the centre of the groups of reflexions lying within 'benzene peaks'.
Compare with 42(i)

to a recognisable group of strong reflexions; purpurogallin again provides an example. The centrosymmetrically-related benzene rings cover only 1/25 by area of the projected unit cell and consequently, on the average, 25 reciprocal-lattice points lie within the main peaks of the benzene transform. Interference from other rings related by symmetry and other constituents of the unit cell will, it is true, reduce or eliminate the intensity at some of the points, but the broad outline of the peak may be recognised. In fig. 43 these 'benzene peaks' may be seen, but it should be noted that the signs of reflexions lying within the peaks are no longer related in a simple way; the region shown in fig. 42(ii) corresponds to the 'benzene peak' just above the inset molecule of fig. 43.

It may be possible to solve some simple structures completely by inspection of the weighted reciprocal-lattice section. For example,

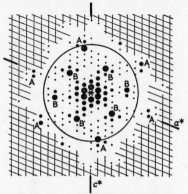

FIG. 44. The $h0l$ section of the weighted reciprocal lattice for coronene

the $h0l$ weighted reciprocal-lattice section of coronene (Robertson and White, 1945) shows a distorted hexagonal arrangement of strong peaks A at about the distance from the origin to be expected from a benzene ring (fig. 44). The distortion indicates that the benzene rings are not parallel to the plane of projection and their inclination to this plane may easily be calculated (Hanson et al, 1953). An inner hexagonal arrangement of strong peaks B suggests that the molecule itself has hexagonal symmetry, and the two indications are definite enough to suggest simply that the molecule consists of 6 benzene rings arranged in a hexagon. This is the molecular structure of coronene.

For more complicated molecules it is usually worthwhile to draw out the weighted reciprocal-lattice section and to study it from the transform standpoint as part of the general preliminary work on a structure. The principle becomes even more effective in three

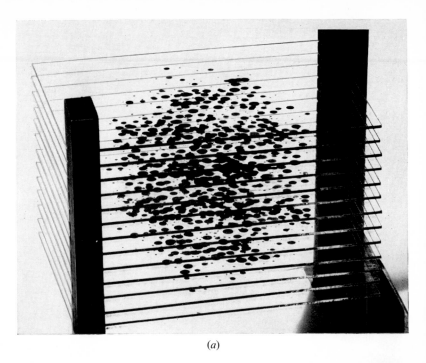

(a)

(b)

FIG. 45. (a) Photograph of a 3-dimensional weighted reciprocal lattice for naphthalene taken in a random direction. (b) Photograph of the same weighted reciprocal lattice taken in a direction perpendicular to the plane of the molecule

dimensions (Kenyon and Taylor, 1953) and it may be possible to recognise chains, rings, and planar groups and to obtain their precise orientations in space (fig. 45).

2.4. *Separation of variables.* One of the problems that sometimes arises in trial-and-error work is that when the exact shape of the molecule is uncertain, stereo-chemical considerations may be insufficient to fix the relative positions of the molecules accurately enough for the work to proceed. A study of the principles of combination of transforms (Chapter 2) permits the separation of the variables of shape and position (Hanson *et al*, 1953; Taylor, 1954). For example, let us suppose that we are studying a structure in which two non-centrosymmetrical molecules are placed in a unit cell of plane group $p2$, so that in two dimensions at least the structure is centrosymmetrical. The transforms of the molecules are identical as regards amplitude (Friedel's law) but because of their centrosymmetrical relationship and their separation in space, the phases are not the same and when the two are added interference occurs and the pattern is crossed by curved lines of zero amplitude (Appendix II, fig. 67(i) and (ii) and section 2.8). It must be noted, however, that this interference cannot produce an *increase* in relative intensity. It follows therefore that a strong peak in the combined transform must correspond to a strong peak in the transform of the single molecule. It is possible then to adjust the shape of the molecule until all the *intense* features of the weighted reciprocal lattice are satisfactorily accounted for without considering the problem of position. Agreement for the weak and absent reflexions will then be poor and the relative positions of the molecules may be adjusted independently by observing only these reflexions. Systematic methods of finding the position giving the best agreement for a given molecular shape have been devised (Taylor, 1954; Vand and Pepinsky, 1956; Crowder, Morley and Taylor, 1958).

3. *Finite and imperfect structures.* In Chapter 3, the various scattering formulae were developed on the assumption that the crystal was infinite and unbounded and that every unit cell was an exact replica of every other one, but these ideals do not always exist even to a first approximation. The Fourier-transform technique is helpful in studying the diffraction effects that arise from various kinds of imperfection. We shall consider only three examples – first the effect of crystal size and shape, secondly the effect of temperature vibrations, and thirdly the effect of faults in layer-like structures.

3.1. *Crystal size and shape.* In Chapter 4 it was shown that a crystal may be considered as the convolution of two functions – one representing the unit-cell contents and the other a lattice peak function representing the crystal lattice. The transform of the complete crystal is the product of the transforms of these two functions. If the crystal is infinite in extent, the transform of the lattice peak function is another lattice peak function; that is, it has a finite intensity only at points of infinitesimal extent. Let us now consider the effect of limiting the extent of the crystal in space. We may consider the small, bounded crystal as the product of the original unbounded crystal with a 'shape-function' which has unit magnitude inside the limits of the crystal and zero outside. The transform of this product is, by the convolution theorem of section **4**.3, the convolution of the transforms of the separate functions – that is, the convolution of the transform of the original unbounded crystal (which was a lattice peak function) with the transform of the shape-function. The reflexions are then no longer confined to infinitesimal points, but each reciprocal-lattice point acquires round it a distribution corresponding to the transform of the shape function – the shape transform (see Appendix II, fig. 70(ii)).

Most crystals are large enough for the shape transform to be smaller in extent than the broadening of the reflexion produced by the instruments used – arising from lack of complete collimation, finite extent of beam, and so on – but it is important to realize the implications of departures from the normal condition. For example, a plate-like crystal – that is one which is effectively unbounded in two dimensions and bounded in the third – has a shape transform that is needle-shaped; it is infinitesimal in extent in directions parallel to the unbounded directions of the plate but of finite extent in a direction parallel to the bounded direction of the plate. Each reciprocal-lattice point thus becomes a streak. As already mentioned, a certain amount of instrumental broadening is already present and in studying shape transforms it is necessary to separate the two effects. The convolution concept can again be used because the X-ray pattern observed is effectively the convolution of the true pattern with a function dependent upon the apparatus. Thus the transform of the X-ray pattern is not the true structure but the true structure multiplied by an instrumental function. Since this function will be the same for different specimens it is possible to isolate it and hence to correct for the effect (Jones, 1938; Stokes, 1948). It is, of course, preferable to avoid the effect altogether and devices such as those used in the study of small-angle scattering may be employed (Guinier and Fournet, 1955). In fact, certain types of small-angle scattering work may be regarded as the observation of the shape transform in the vicinity of the origin point of the reciprocal lattice.

3.2. Temperature effects. A further assumption that was made in deriving the scattering formula for the complete crystal was that all the atoms are stationary with respect to each other. Because of thermal vibration this assumption is not correct and the modifications produced have been discussed from time to time in great detail (Debye, 1914; Waller, 1923; Faxén, 1923; Lonsdale and Smith, 1941, etc.). The present section is intended only to indicate how the application of Fourier-transform theory can give an immediate qualitative appreciation of the effects produced.

Let us consider the simplest kind of structure, having a single atom at each lattice point and being of effectively infinite extent. If all the atoms are stationary with respect to the lattice points, the resulting diffraction pattern has zero intensity everywhere except precisely at the points of the reciprocal lattice. If, however, the atoms vibrate about their mean positions the pattern is modified. The frequency of thermal vibration is likely to be very small indeed compared with the frequency of the X-radiation used and the result at any instant is as though the atoms were stationary but displaced in various ways from the lattice points. We require therefore to find the diffraction pattern of a structure consisting of atoms lying near to, but not precisely at, the points of a lattice.

In order to deduce the resulting transform it is necessary first to describe the structure in terms of its component features. Suppose that we select from the infinite lattice all the atoms which, at some instant of time, are displaced by the same amount in the same direction from the lattice points (figs. 48*a* and *b* illustrate this in two dimensions). These atoms lie on a perfectly regular lattice of the same dimensions as the main lattice, but displaced relative to it; and the whole crystal, at that precise instant, may be expressed as the sum of a large number of arrangements like 48*b*. The arrangement of 48*b* can, in turn, be described as the product of an arrangement with atoms at *every* point of a perfect lattice and a random distribution which is zero except over certain randomly arranged regions where its value is unity (fig. 48*c*). The transform of 48*b* is, by the convolution theorem, the convolution of the transform of the perfect lattice – that is a set of infinitesimal peaks on reciprocal-lattice points – and the transform of 48*c*. Since 48*c* is a completely random arrangement of regions for which contributions will be all in phase only at the origin, its transform consists of a central intense peak surrounded by a uniform distribution of intensity, the extent of which depends on the size of the separate regions in 48*c*. If – as shown by the small circles in the diagram – the average size of the regions is less than that of a unit cell, so that no two adjacent atoms are displaced in the same way, the extent of the continuous background is greater than a reciprocal unit cell and the resulting con-

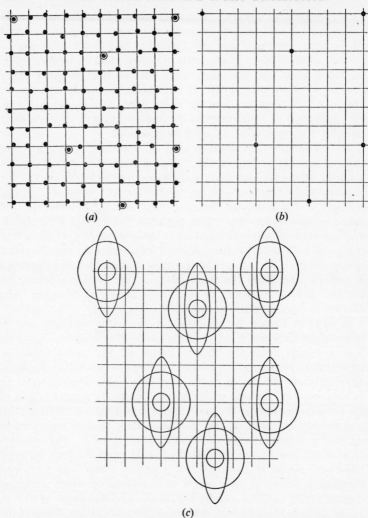

(a)   (b)

(c)

FIG. 48. (a) Instantaneous positions of atoms in a simple structure displaced from their lattice points by thermal vibration. The ringed atoms are assumed to be displaced by the same amount in the same direction. (b) The ringed atoms lie on a regular lattice identical with the original one but displaced from it. (c) The arrangement of fig. 48b may be regarded as the product of the basic lattice (with an atom at every point) and a function which is zero everywhere except within the small circles shown on this figure where it is unity. If, as is more likely in practice, the atoms do not vibrate independently the function may be unity within larger circles (for isotropic materials) or ellipses (for anisotropic materials).

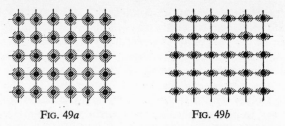

FIG. 49a   FIG. 49b

FIG. 49. (a) The appearance of the reciprocal lattice when the applicable function is that of the larger circles of fig. 48c. (b) The appearance of the reciprocal lattice when the applicable function is that of the elliptical regions of fig. 48c

volution is simply a set of sharp peaks at reciprocal-lattice points with a continuous background.

To find the transform of the complete crystal at this instant we must now add the transforms of the various sets of atoms like that of 48b. They each consist of peaks on a continuous background but there are phase differences between each set because of the different displacements. Each arrangement like 48b has a displacement which is small compared with a unit cell and consequently the phase differences become important only at large distances from the origin of reciprocal space. Thus the total effect is that a continuous background is introduced; and since this is random for each component, the phase differences do not affect it and it remains at a level governed only by the scattering factor for non-vibrating atoms. The sharp peaks, however, fall in intensity with distance from the origin, the effect being similar to that of increasing the size of the atoms.

In practice it is unlikely that adjacent atoms vibrate independently. Consequently, the regions of fig. 48c tend to be larger than one unit cell and hence the continuous part of its transform extends over much less than one reciprocal unit cell. Thus the convolution representing the transform of 48b is a set of sharp peaks, each surrounded by a diffuse region. If the extent of the regions is the same in all directions (the large circles of 48c) these diffuse regions are circular (fig. 49a), but if the elastic properties of the crystal are such that linking of vibrations in one direction is more likely than that in another (the ellipses of 48c) the regions of 48c are no longer roughly circular and the diffuse regions surrounding reciprocal-lattice points are also no longer circular (fig. 49b).

The shape of diffuse regions surrounding reciprocal-lattice points can thus be seen to be the transform of the average shape of the regions of fig. 48c which in turn is related to the elastic properties of the crystal.

The problem is, of course, complicated still further if there are many atoms associated with a unit cell and consideration must then be given to the possibility of molecular vibration as well as atomic vibration. If, for example, the whole molecule is displaced without change of orientation in a completely random way, then the structure can be represented roughly as the convolution of that already described (48a) with a single molecule and the resulting transform of 48c has to be multiplied by the transform of the molecule. The intensity of the diffuse regions is thus modified by that of the transform. These ideas may possibly explain the electron-diffraction photographs of anthracene taken by Charlesby, Finch and Wilman (1939). These photographs show, in addition to the main diffraction spots, a considerable variation of the background which the authors claim to be the Fourier transform of the unit-cell contents. They could not be more definite, however, because of difficulties associated with orienting the crystal, the unit cell of which contains two molecules.

3.3. *Stacking disorder in layer structures.* Stacking faults occurring in layer structures give rise to interesting diffraction effects (Edwards and Lipson, 1942; Wilson, 1949a; Cowley, 1953b, etc.) which may be conveniently studied by Fourier-transform methods.

Let us consider the example of cobalt (Edwards and Lipson, 1942; Wilson, 1942) for which each layer consists of a close-packed-hexagonal arrangement of atoms. If two layers are placed together with

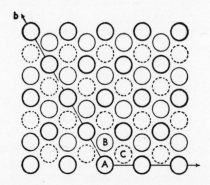

FIG. 50. Relative atomic positions for the three possible layers
A, B, C

the closest possible packing, a third layer may be added in one of two ways; its atoms may occupy sites immediately above those of the first layer or they may occupy an alternative set of sites. Fig. 50 shows that there are, in all, three types of layer – those with atoms vertically above sites marked A, B and C respectively. If only two kinds of layer occur, stacked alternately, then the result is a close-packed-hexagonal structure; if all three are used, stacked in sequence, the result is a close-packed-cubic structure, the layers being in (111) planes. Occasionally, samples are found in which the two kinds of stacking are mixed, and then streaks occur in the X-ray diffraction patterns.

The problem may be studied in two dimensions. In fig. 51, the layers are represented by rows of equally spaced dots. The different

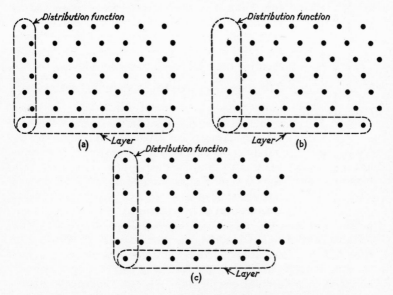

FIG. 51. Two-dimensional representations of possible stacking showing the layers and the 'distribution functions' (a) for hexagonal stacking, (b) for cubic stacking, and (c) for random stacking

layer positions correspond to displacements of one-third of the distance between a pair of atoms in either direction. Thus figs. 51a, 51b and 51c represent hexagonal packing, cubic packing and random stacking respectively.

The Fourier transforms of these arrangements may be derived in the following way. In each example the structure may be described as the convolution of a single layer with a distribution function indicating which of the three positions is adopted. The layer and the distribution function are indicated by dotted lines in figures 51a, b and c. The transform of the layer is a set of lines perpendicular to the layer and with a spacing reciprocal to the separation of the points in the layer. If the layer is of infinite extent, the lines are of infinitesimal thickness. The transform of the whole is the product of this with the transform of the distribution function. We see immediately, therefore, that no matter what the order of the layers, no spots or streaks can occur except along the lines of the transform of the layer. It is therefore necessary to consider the transform of the distribution function only along these lines. The distribution function may be considered as the sum of three functions – all the dots on row 1, all the dots on row 2 and all the dots on row 3 (fig. 52). The transforms of these add together with phase differences corresponding to their relative displacements. If we number the lines of the transform of the layer from the centre outwards, then for rows 0, 3, 6, etc., they are in phase, for 1, 4, 7 they are $\frac{2\pi}{3}$ out of phase, and for 2, 5, 8 they are $\frac{4\pi}{3}$ out of phase. Thus, for the rows 0, 3, 6, etc., there would be no change if all the dots were in the same column. Since there is only *one* dot on each row, it follows that, *whatever* the arrangement of stacking, the transform of the distribution function, as far as rows 0, 3, 6, etc., are concerned, is the transform of a vertical line of dots – i.e. a set of horizontal streaks. The product of the transforms is thus a set of sharp

FIG. 52.
The three components of the distribution function

peaks. For the rows in between, the result depends on the order of stacking and, if this is random, the possibility of streaks along the rows 1, 2, 4, 5, etc., arises. If the transform of a particular kind of stacking is to be calculated, the foregoing analysis shows that it is necessary to perform the computation only over very small regions of reciprocal space – namely, along rows 1, 2, 4, 5, etc. A further reduction in the region to be computed can be made as follows. If we consider the distribution function, for a moment, to consist of the product of a set of three complete rows with a function eliminating two out of three atoms in every row, it can be seen that the result is the convolution of the two transforms, which in turn means that the intensity distribution along the rows is a periodic function with a repeat distance reciprocal to the layer spacing.

Since there are only three x coordinates possible in the distribution function and the y coordinates are successive multiples of a unit translation, and it is necessary to compute only over a short length of rows 1 and 2, the calculation, even for a very large number of layers, becomes quite reasonable.

In fig. 53 the intensity distribution over this region has been plotted (*a*) for cubic packing, (*b*) for hexagonal packing and (*c*) for a random arrangement of 100 layers.

4. *Modern techniques.* One or two examples will now be given of the use of Fourier transform ideas in giving a qualitative, physical, introduction to various modern techniques.

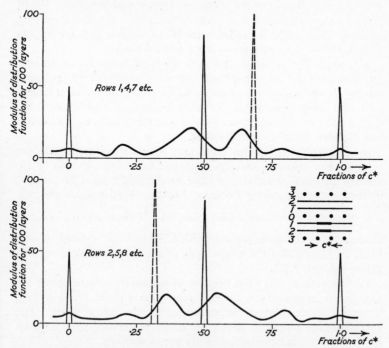

FIG. 53. The transform of the distribution functions calculated over one reciprocal repeat distance for rows 1 and 2 of the diffraction pattern (*a*) (thin line) for hexagonal stacking, (*b*) (dotted line) for cubic stacking and (*c*) (thick line) for a random arrangement of 100 layers. The inset figure shows the two portions for which the calculation has been made

4.1. *Intensity statistics.* Since the earliest work by Wilson (1949*b*) a considerable study has been made of the statistical distribution of the intensities to be expected for various kinds of structures. The physical basis can easily be understood by reference to transform theory. For example, the Fourier transform of a non-centrosymmetric molecule (see Appendix I, fig. 63(i)) consists of rather diffuse peaks which merge into one another more or less continuously without passing through zero; in fact the modulus is zero only at a number of isolated points. For a centrosymmetric structure, however, (See Appendix I, fig. 62(i)) the two centrosymmetrically related parts each have an identical transform of the type just described but, when the transforms are added, interference between the two occurs and lines of zero intensity cross the pattern. The relative proportions of high, medium and zero intensities are thus changed (Taylor, 1952b). The presence of *two* centrosymmetrical units in a centrosymmetrical relationship produces still more interference and a further disturbance of the statistics (Lipson and Woolfson, 1952); Wilson has called such a distribution 'bicentric'. Further symmetry elements clearly produce other types of interference and Rogers and Wilson (1953) have now produced a general theory.

It is important to notice that it is the total symmetry in the *unit* cell that matters and not just the repetitive symmetry of the space group. It is possible, for example, to have centrosymmetric (Herbstein and Schoening, 1957) and even bicentrosymmetric molecules in non-centrosymmetric space groups and these give rise to centric and bicentric intensity distributions.

In an acentric transform there may exist certain parts that are centric. For example, the region around the origin tends to be so, and for this reason reflexions close to the origin must be omitted in testing for acentricity (Wilson, 1949b). Wilson gives the rule that reflexions with values of sin θ less than $\frac{\lambda}{a}$, where a is the unit cell dimension in the direction concerned, should be omitted; it can easily be shown that the origin peak of a transform has about this extent (section 7.2.3).

Centric regions can exist because of symmetry relationships; for example, if an atomic arrangement has a mirror plane, the transform is centric along the line perpendicular to the mirror plane. The corresponding reflexions should therefore be omitted from any test for distinguishing between centricity and acentricity.

We can also see why systematically absent reflexions must not be used in such tests; they represent points in reciprocal space where the amplitude is necessarily zero and therefore are not true sampling points of the transform.

4.2. *Inequalities and sign relationships.* In crystal-structure work the reflexions often tend to be treated as separate entities with no apparent relationship to each other. The introduction of the subject through Fourier transforms immediately eliminates this idea and it is not so surprising to find that relationships exist when the structure factors are considered as samples at particular points of a basic transform.

As a simple example, we know that the origin peak of a transform is positive, although it should be remembered that this result is simply a convention based upon the rule – not always obeyed – that all atoms scatter in phase. If a strong peak exists elsewhere in the transform, then a high proportion of the atoms must lie near to a set of planes reciprocally related to the vector distance of the transform peak from the origin. The peak, however, may be positive or negative, depending upon whether the set of planes passes through the origin or is symmetrically disposed about it. If another strong transform peak lies half way between the origin and the first peak, then the atoms must also lie near to a set of planes of twice the

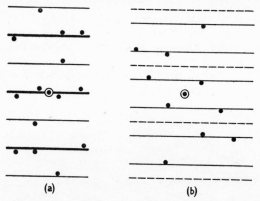

(a)   (b)

Fig. 55. Illustration of the physical basis of one of the simplest inequalities. In (a) a centrosymmetrical arrangement of atoms lying near to a set of planes, one of which passes through the origin, would give rise to a positive peak in the transform; it is possible for the same set of atoms to lie close to a set of planes of twice the spacing (heavier lines) and hence to give a peak of half the distance from the origin of reciprocal space. In (b) a centro-symmetrical arrangement of atoms lying near to a set of planes, none of which passes through the origin, would give a negative peak in the transform; it is impossible for the atoms also to lie close to a set of planes of twice the spacing (dotted lines)

spacing of the first; from fig. 55 we can see that they can do so only if the first set of planes passes through the origin. Thus the sign of the first peak must be positive irrespective of whether the sign of the second is positive or negative.

This result is merely a qualitative statement of the simplest of the inequalities found by Harker and Kasper (1948), who say that if the first and second order reflexions from a given set of planes are both strong, then the second order is probably positive irrespective of the sign of the first.

This result has been generalized by Sayre (1952) and Cochran (1952) in the form that, if three reflexions of indices (h, k, l), (h', k', l'), and $(h + h', k + k', l + l')$ are all strong, then the sign of $F(hkl)$ tends to be the same as the product of the signs of the other two structure factors. (The result just discussed can be obtained by putting $h = h'$ etc. in the above relationship.) From the transform point of view, this relationship may be understood by considering the texture of transforms. All transforms appear to be built up of arrangements of regions of characteristic sizes and shapes. It follows that for a centrosymmetrical structure if one starts at any two points in reciprocal space and travels the same distance in the same direction from each, a similar sequence of regions will be traversed and hence the same number of zero lines will be crossed on the average. If the starting and finishing points are on very weak regions there will be some ambiguity, but if both start and finish lie at the centre of strong peaks then the sign relationship becomes much more definite.

Thus, for example, in fig. 56 the sign-changes in going from A to B will be the same in number as those in going from C to D.

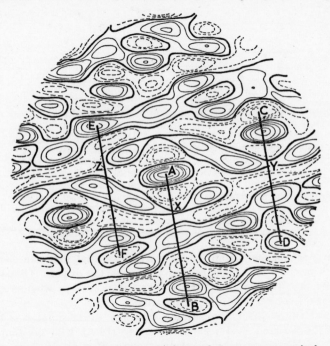

Fig. 56. The calculated transform of a centrosymmetrical arrangement of ten atoms (see fig. 62(i), Appendix I) used to illustrate sign relationships

This could be expressed by the statement $s_A \times s_B = s_C \times s_D$, where s_A indicates 'sign of A' etc. It should be noted that at the points X and Y the zero contours approach each other, but at the point Z the zero contour is not crossed at all. Thus, although the actual number of sign changes is different for EF, it is still an odd number and the final sign relationship holds. When the transform is sampled by the reciprocal lattice this clearly leads to relationships between signs of reflexions. For example,

$$s(0, 0) \times s(h, k) = s(h', k') \times s(h + h', k + k') \qquad (57.1)$$

or, since $s(0, 0)$ is positive always,

$$s(h, k) = s(h', k') \times s(h + h', k + k'). \qquad (57.2)$$

In fig. 56, if A is $(0, 0)$, B is (h, k), C is (h', k') and D is $(h + h', k + k')$, then $s(h, k)$ is negative, $s(h', k')$ is negative, $s(h + h', k + k')$ is positive and the relationship is clearly obeyed.

5 *Conclusion.* This chapter has only skimmed the surface of transform-theory application and it is hoped that it will have provided sufficient indication of the power and versatility of the approach to stimulate further study.

As has already been indicated, one of the outstanding points is that the same comparatively small amount of basic theory may be used in a large number of diverse problems, providing a constant reminder that in all the various branches of X-ray diffraction the central problem is the relationship between an object and its diffraction pattern, the relationship between real and reciprocal space, the relationship described as Fourier transformation.

E

CALCULATION OF TRANSFORMS

For the purpose of calculation, equation *9.2*

$$G(S) = \sum_{n=1}^{N} f_n(S) \exp 2\pi i \mathbf{r}_n \cdot \mathbf{S}$$

for the transform of a group of atoms is not very convenient. Although the transform is a continuous function, it must obviously be calculated at a set of discrete points and the simplest way to achieve this is to place the molecules or group of atoms in an arbitrary unit cell. The structure factors computed from equation *17.2*

$$F(h,k,l) = \sum_{n=1}^{N} f_n \exp 2\pi i(hx_n + ky_n + lz_n)$$

then give the values of the tranforms at a set of discrete points – the reciprocal-lattice points. The arbitrary unit cell in real space is chosen to suit the problem; the larger it is, the smaller will be the reciprocal cell, that is, the closer will be the points at which the transform is calculated.

It is usual to compute the real and imaginary parts separately (section *2.6*) using the equations:

$$A = \sum_{n=1}^{N} f_n \cos 2\pi(hx_n + ky_n + lz_n),$$

$$B = \sum_{n=1}^{N} f_n \sin 2\pi(hx_n + ky_n + lz_n).$$

The amplitude is given by $|G| = |\sqrt{A^2 + B^2}|$ and the phase angle ϕ by $\cos \phi = \dfrac{A}{|\sqrt{A^2 + B^2}|}$ and $\sin \phi = \dfrac{B}{|\sqrt{A^2 + B^2}|}$. It is important to notice that these two equations taken separately each have two solutions for ϕ between 0° and 360° but only one is common to both; for this reason, the equation $\tan \phi = \dfrac{B}{A}$ alone is not sufficient.

To illustrate some of the properties of transforms a non-centro-symmetrical arrangement of atoms has been selected and various computations have been performed for it. Fig. 59 shows the arrangement of atoms, the arbitrary unit cell chosen for the computation and the two different origins used. Table 59 gives the coordinates for the hypothetical structure.

The values of A, B, $|\sqrt{A^2+B^2}|$ and ϕ were calculated for both origins and for all values of h and k between -30 and $+30$ using the Manchester University digital computer. The results are presented as contour maps in figs. 60-63.

TABLE 59

Fractional coordinates of the atoms shown in fig. 59 with respect to the two different origins.

Atom	Origin 1		Origin 2	
	x/a	y/b	x/a	y/b
1	$+0.050$	$+0.000$	$+0.180$	$+0.023$
2	$+0.010$	$+0.040$	$+0.140$	$+0.063$
3	-0.049	$+0.063$	$+0.081$	$+0.086$
4	-0.050	$+0.000$	$+0.080$	$+0.023$
5	-0.022	-0.085	$+0.108$	-0.062
6	$+0.022$	-0.062	$+0.152$	-0.039

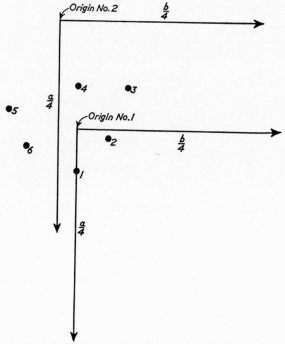

FIG. 59. Hypothetical molecule of six atoms for which the transforms in succeeding figures have been calculated; two different origins and the unit cell chosen for computation are indicated.

FIG. 60 (i) Real part of the transform of the hypothetical molecule with respect to origin number 1; the heavy line is the zero contour and the negative contours are dotted

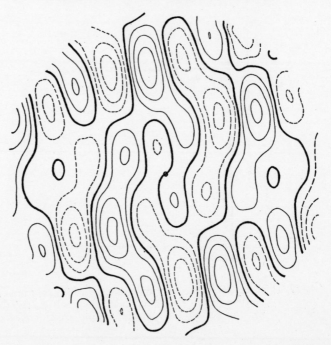

FIG. 60 (ii) Imaginary part of the transform of the hypothetical molecule with respect to origin number 1; the heavy line is the zero contour and the negative contours are dotted

FIG. 61 (i). Modulus of the transform of the hypothetical molecule with respect to origin number 1; the lowest regions are shaded and the black spots are points of zero amplitude

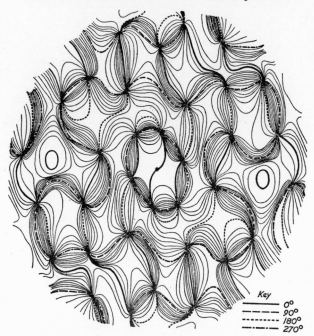

FIG. 61 (ii). Phase of the transform of the hypothetical molecule with respect to origin number 1; contours are shown at intervals of 10°, the 0°, 90°, 180°, and 270° lines being distinguished as illustrated in the key

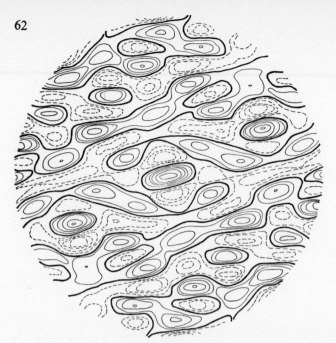

FIG. 62 (i). Real part of the transform of the hypothetical molecule with respect to origin number 2; the heavy lines are the zero
contours and the negative contours are dotted

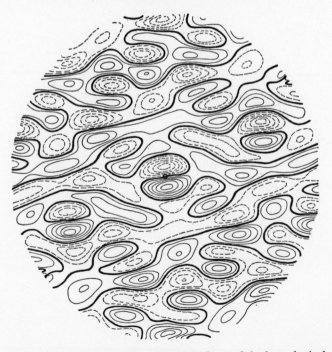

FIG. 62 (ii). Imaginary part of the transform of the hypothetical
molecule with respect to origin number 2; the heavy lines are the
zero contours and the negative contours are dotted

FIG. 63 (i). Modulus of the transform of the hypothetical molecule with respect to origin number 2; the lowest regions are shaded
and the black spots are points of zero amplitude

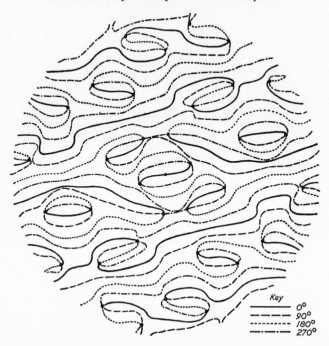

FIG. 63 (ii). Phase of the transform of the hypothetical molecule with respect to origin number 2; only the 0°, 90°, 180° and 270°
contours are shown in order to avoid confusion

Among the points of interest arising from these diagrams the following are of special importance. First, the modulus diagrams (61(i) and 63(i)) are identical; the choice of origin has no effect on the intensity of the scattered radiation. Secondly, the structure is non-centrosymmetrical and the amplitude becomes zero only at a number of discrete points; the real parts (60(i) and 62(i)) may be regarded as modulus diagrams for centrosymmetrical structures formed by adding a second centrosymmetrically-related group to the first and they both have *line* zeros. Thirdly, the zero contours of the real parts of a transform are the 90° and 270° contours of the phase diagrams and the zero contours of the imaginary parts are the 0° and 180° contours of the phase diagrams. The points of intersection of the contours are the point zeros of the modulus diagram at which the phase is indeterminate. The phase diagrams for the two origins are completely different but the points of indeterminacy must be the same for both. Fourthly, the behaviour of the phase contours in the immediate vicinity of the points of indeterminacy is of interest; a small circular path traversed round one of these points will pass through all possible phase angles in sequence from 0° through 90°. 180° 270° and 0° again.

APPENDIX II

OPTICAL TRANSFORMS

As mentioned in Chapter 5, the concept of the reciprocal solid and the sphere of reflexion applies to all diffraction problems. With visible light, if, as in optical transform methods (Hanson *et al*, 1953, etc.), objects with dimensions about 10,000 × the wavelength are used, the sphere of reflexion may be regarded as planar with respect to the portions of the transform that are of interest. It is thus possible to observe a complete cross-section of the transform of an object without rotation of the object, as is needed in X-ray studies. A card with holes punched to represent the positions of atoms in the projection of a crystal structure will, if placed in the parallel beam of a suitably designed spectrometer, produce a diffraction pattern which is a cross-section of its transform. Only the intensity can be recorded photographically and the result is often referred to as an optical transform. A diagram of the apparatus – now known as an optical diffractometer – is shown in fig. 65 and some examples of diffraction patterns are shown in figs. 67, 68, 69 and 70(ii). Full size photographs of the masks used are shown in fig. 70(i).

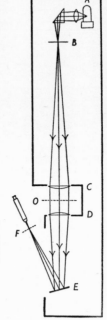

FIG. 65. Schematic diagram of an optical diffractometer. A is the light source, B is the pinhole, C and D are the lenses, and E is an optically flat mirror; the diffraction pattern of an object placed at O is seen in the plane F

65

66

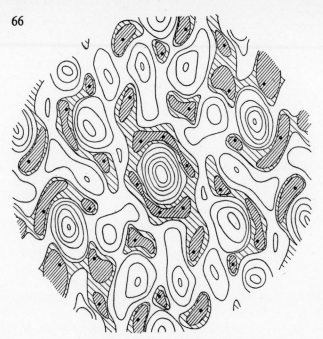

FIG. 66 (i). Repeat of 61(i) for ease of comparison with 67(i) opposite

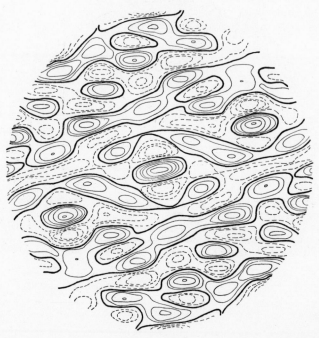

FIG. 66 (ii). Repeat of 62(i) for ease of comparison with 67(ii) opposite

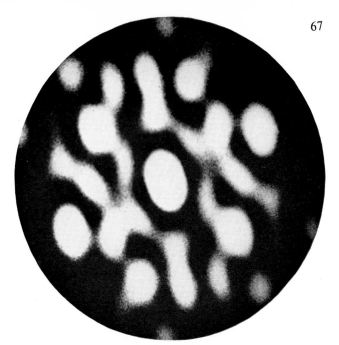

FIG. 67 (i). Optical transform of the hypothetical arrangement of six atoms as used for the calculations in Appendix I. (The mask used is shown in fig. 70(i)*a*)

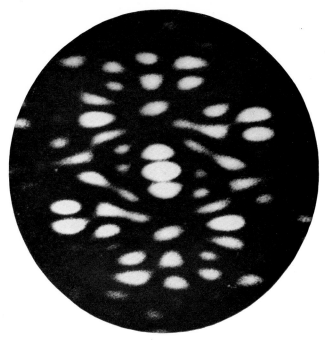

FIG. 67 (ii). Optical transform of two centrosymmetrically-related units equivalent to the real part of the transform shown in 67(i) (The mask used is shown in fig. 70(i)*b*)

68

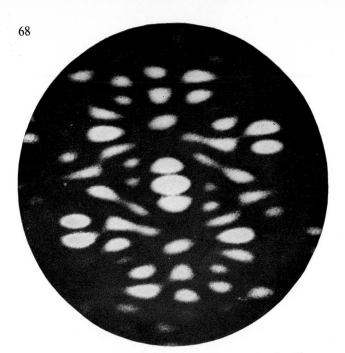

FIG. 68 (i). Repeat of 67(ii) (for ease of comparison). The two centrosymmetrically-related units are now regarded as the contents of a single unit cell

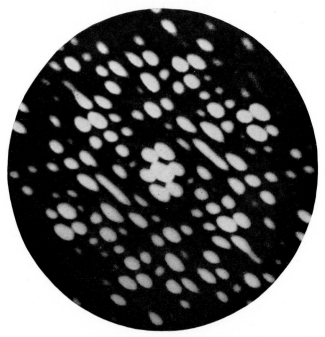

FIG. 68 (ii). Optical transform of two adjacent unit cells as for 68(i). (The mask used is shown in 70(i)c)

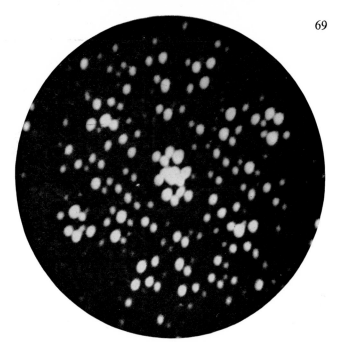

FIG. 69 (i). Optical transform of four adjacent unit cells as for 68(i). (The mask used is shown in 70(i)*d*)

FIG. 69. (ii) Optical transform of many unit cells as for 68(i) (The mask used is shown in 70(i)*e*)

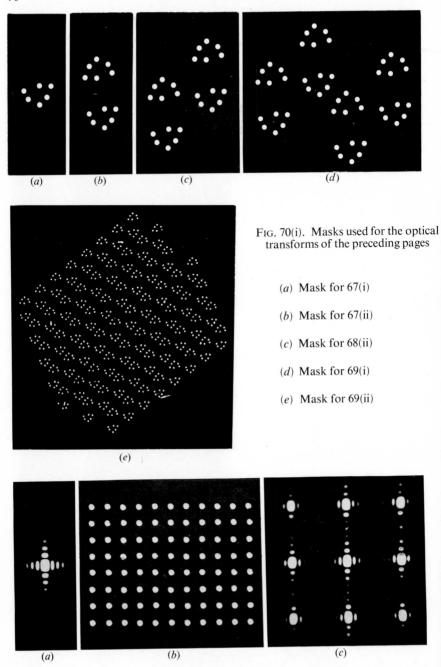

Fig. 70(i). Masks used for the optical transforms of the preceding pages

(a) Mask for 67(i)

(b) Mask for 67(ii)

(c) Mask for 68(ii)

(d) Mask for 69(i)

(e) Mask for 69(ii)

(e)

(a)   (b)   (c)

Fig. 70 (ii). (a) Optical diffraction pattern of a rectangular aperture. (b) Mask representing the product of a lattice function with a function representing the aperture of 70a. (c) Optical diffraction pattern of mask shown in 70(ii)b

APPENDIX III

SOME RELATIONSHIPS BETWEEN THE CALCULATED TRANSFORMS OF APPENDIX I, THE OPTICAL TRANSFORMS OF APPENDIX II, AND THE MAIN TEXT OF THE MONOGRAPH

The units used for figs. 67, 68 and 69 are the same as those used for the calculated transforms in Appendix I, and the separation of the units from the centre of symmetry in 67(ii) is the same as the displacement of origin number 2 for the calculated transforms. Thus fig. 67(i) should compare with fig. 61(i) (repeated as 66(i) for convenience in comparison) and 67(ii) should compare with 62(i) (repeated as 66(ii) for convenience in comparison).

The following points from the main text may be illustrated by comparison of various figures in the Appendices.

The effect of the choice of origin (section 2.7) can be seen by comparing figs. 60, 61, 62 and 63.

Straight fringes (section 2.9) are shown by fig. 68(ii) and 'wavy' fringes are shown by figs. 66(ii) and 67(ii).

The evolution of the reciprocal lattice and its relationship to the transform on one unit cell (section 3.3) are illustrated by figs. 68 and 69.

Straight fringes which could give rise to systematic absences if coincident with certain reciprocal lattice rows (section 3.5) are shown in fig. 68(ii).

The theorem that the transform of the convolution of two functions is the product of their separate transforms is illustrated by comparing figs. 68(i) and 69(ii). 68(i) is the transform of a unit of structure and 69(ii) is the transform of the convolution of this structure with a regular lattice (Chapter 4).

The theorem that the transform of the product of two functions is the convolution of their separate transforms is illustrated by fig. 70(ii) (Chapter 4).

The change in the 'texture' of a transform as the shape and size of the object in real space change (section 7.2.3) is illustrated by comparing figs. 67, 68 and 69(i).

The effect of the shape of a small crystal is illustrated by fig. 70(ii) (section 7.3.1).

The differences in intensity distribution for centrosymmetrical and non-centrosymmetrical structures (section 7.4.1) may be seen by comparing fig. 66(i) with 66(ii) and fig. 67(i) with 67(ii).

71

REFERENCES

Beevers, C. A. & Robertson, J. H., 1950.   Acta Cryst. **3**, 164   -   36
Bernal, J. D., 1926.   Proc. Roy. Soc. A. **151**, 384   -   -   - 4, 28
Bijvoet, J. M.   *See* Bokhoven, C.
Bokhoven, C., Schoone, J. C., & Bijvoet, J. M., 1951.   Acta Cryst. **4**, 275   -   -   -   -   -   -   - 34
Bragg, W. L., 1913.   Proc. Camb. Phil. Soc. **17**, 43 -   -   - 31
Bragg, W. L., & West, J., 1930.   Phil. Mag. **10**, 823-   -   - 38
Buerger, M. J., 1944.   *The Photography of the Reciprocal Lattice.*   Cambridge, Mass.   A.S.X.R.E.D. -   -   -   -   - 30
Buerger, M. J., 1951.   Acta Cryst. **4**, 531 -   -   -   - 36

Charlesby, A., Finch, G. I. & Wilman, H., 1939.   Proc. Phys. Soc. **51**, 479   -   -   -   -   -   -   - 5, 50
Cochran, W., 1952.   Acta Cryst. **5**, 65   -   -   -   - 55
Cochran, W.   *See also* Lipson, H.
Cowley, J. M., 1953a.   Acta Cryst. **6**, 516   -   -   - 29
Cowley, J. M., 1953b.   Acta Cryst. **6**, 522   -   -   - 50
Crowder, M. M., Morley, K. A. & Taylor, C. A., 1958, *Nature*, **180**, 431   45

Debye, P., 1914.   Ann. d. Physik. **43**, 49 -   -   -   - 47

Edwards, O. S., & Lipson, H., 1942.   Proc. Roy. Soc. A. **180**, 268   - 50
Ewald, P. P., 1940.   Proc. Phys. Soc. **52**, 167   -   - 9, 22, 24

Faxén, H., 1923.   Zeits. f. Physik. **17**, 266-   -   -   - 47
Finch, G. I.   *See* Charlesby, A.
Fournet, G.   *See* Guinier, A.
Friedrich, W., Knipping, P. & Laue, M., 1912.   Sitzb. math. phys. Klasse bayer. Akad. Wiss. München, p. 303 -   -   -   - 30

Guinier, A. & Fournet, G., 1955.   *Small-angle scattering of X-rays.*   New York; Wiley.   -   -   -   -   - 46

Hanson, A. W., Lipson, H. & Taylor, C. A., 1953.   Proc. Roy. Soc. A. **218**, 371 -   -   -   -   - 18, 40, 43, 44, 45, 65
Harker, D. & Kasper, J. S., 1948.   Acta Cryst. **1**, 70   -   - 55
Henry, N. F. M., Lipson, H. & Wooster, W. A., 1951.   *Interpretation of X-ray Diffraction Photographs.*   London; Macmillan   -   - 32
Herbstein, F. H. & Schoening, F. R. L., 1957.   Acta Cryst, **10**, 657   - 54
Hettich, A., 1935.   Zeits. f. Krist. **90**, 473   -   -   - 9

Jaeger, J. C., 1949.   *An Introduction to the Laplace transformation.*   London: Methuen -   -   -   -   -   - 23
Jones, F. W., 1938.   Proc. Roy. Soc. A. **166**, 16   -   -   - 46

Kasper, J. S.   *See* Harker, D.
Kenyon, P. A. & Taylor, C. A., 1953.   Acta Cryst. **6**, 745 - - 45
Klug, A., 1950a.   Acta Cryst. **3**, 165 - - - - 37
Klug, A., 1950b.   Acta Cryst. **3**, 176 - - - 9, 10, 40
Knipping, P.   *See* Friedrich, W.
Knott, G., 1940.   Proc. Phys. Soc. **52**, 229 - - 9, 10, 40

Laue, M.   *See* Friedrich, W.
Lipson, H. & Cochran, W., 1953.   *The Determination of Crystal Structures.*
   London: Bell - - - - - 10
Lipson, H. & Taylor, C. A., 1951.   Acta Cryst. **4**, 458 - - 10
Lipson, H. & Woolfson, M. M., 1952.   Acta Cryst. **5**, 680 - - 54
Lipson, H.   *See also* Edwards, O. S., Hanson, A. W., Henry, N. F. M., Pinnock,
   P. R.
Lonsdale, K. & Smith, N., 1941.   Proc. Roy. Soc. A. **179**, 8 - - 47

Morley, K. A., & Taylor, C. A., 1957.   J. Sci. Instrum. **34**, 54 - 40
Morley, K. A.   *See also* Crowder, M. M.

Patterson, A. L., 1934.   Phys. Rev. **46**, 372 - - - 34
Pepinsky, R.   *See* Vand, V.
Pinnock, P. R. & Taylor, C. A., 1955.   Acta Cryst. **8**, 687 - - 40
Pinnock, P. R., Taylor, C. A. & Lipson, H., 1956.   Acta Cryst. **9**, 173 - 37

Robertson, J. H.,   *See* Beevers, C. A.
Robertson, J. M., 1933.   Proc. Roy. Soc. A. **142**, 659 - - 42
Robertson, J. M. & White, J. G., 1945.   J. Chem. Soc., 607 - - 44
Robertson, J. M. & Woodward, I., 1940.   J. Chem. Soc., 36 - - 34
Rogers, D. & Wilson, A. J. C., 1953.   Acta Cryst. **6**, 439 - - 54

Sayre, D. M., 1952.   Acta Cryst. **5**, 60 - - - - 55
Schoening, F. R. L.   *See* Herbstein, F. H.
Schoone, J. C.   *See* Bokhoven, C.
Smith, H.   *See* Lonsdale, K.
Stadler, H. P., 1953.   Acta Cryst. **6**, 540 - - - 10
Stokes, A. R. 1948, Proc. Phys. Soc. **61**, 382 - - - 46

Taylor, C. A., 1952a.   Nature **169**, 1086 - - - - 43
Taylor, C. A., 1952b.   Acta Cryst. **5**, 141 - - - - 54
Taylor, C. A., 1954.   Acta Cryst. **7**, 757 - - - - 45
Taylor, C. A.   *See also* Crowder, M. M., Hanson, A. W., Kenyon, P. A.,
   Lipson, H., Morley, K. A., Pinnock, P. R.
Titchmarsh, E. C., 1948.   *Introduction to the Theory of Fourier Integrals.*
   Oxford: Clarendon Press - - - - - 20

Vand, V. & Pepinsky, R., 1956.   Zeits. f. Krist. **108**, 1 - - 45

Waller, I., 1923.   Zeits. f. Physik. **17**, 398 - - - 47
West, J.   *See* Bragg, W. L.

White, J. G.   *See* Robertson, J. M.
Wilman, H.   *See* Charlesby, A.
Wilson, A. J. C., 1942.   Proc. Roy. Soc. A. **180**, 277   -   -   50
Wilson, A. J. C., 1949a.   *X-ray Optics*.   London; Methuen   -   50
Wilson, A. J. C., 1949b.   Acta Cryst. **2**, 318   -   -   7, 53, 54
Wilson, A. J. C.   *See also* Rogers, D.
Woodward, I.   *See* Robertson, J. M.
Woolfson, M. M.   *See* Lipson, H.
Wooster, W. A.   *See* Henry, N. F. M.

SUBJECT INDEX